BUILDING BLOCKS OF THE UNIVERSE

Isaac Asimov

ABELARD-SCHUMAN
London New York Toronto

BUILDING

4119

BLOCKS

OF THE

UNIVERSE

REVISED EDITION

Printed in the United States of America

LONDON	NEW YORK	TORONTO
Abelard-Schuman	*Abelard-Schuman*	*Abelard-Schuman*
Limited	*Limited*	*Canada Limited*
8 King Street	*6 West 57th Street*	*81 John Street*

To Lillian and Theodore McClintock,
for unfailing help and cooperation.

CONTENTS

The Hundred and Two

When scientists talk of *matter*, they mean anything at all that has weight—a rock, a human being, a book, a pail of sea water, or an automobile. Almost anything else you can name, including the sun, the moon, and the stars, is matter. Even the air has weight and is matter. (Such things as light, heat, x-rays, and radio waves have no weight and are, therefore, not matter.)

All matter is made up of tiny particles. These particles are so small that they cannot be seen with any microscope invented so far. They are called *atoms*.

As we look about, it must seem to us that there are thousands of different kinds of matter in the world. It may be surprising, then, to learn that the number of different kinds of atoms out of which all this variety is made is not very large. The kinds of atoms we know about, in fact, are only 102 in number. What's more, most of these 102 kinds of atoms are very rare. Some do not exist in nature at all; they are found only in the laboratories where scientists have made them. Only a dozen kinds of atoms are really what you might call common.

Atoms sometimes exist as separate particles without any special connection to other particles. Mostly, however, they form groups. Such groups of atoms are known as *molecules*.

These groups stick together, more or less, as time passes. This behavior is similar, in some ways, to the behavior of human beings.

Some people may live all by themselves, but most form part of a family. Although there are only two kinds of human beings, males and females, there are many different kinds of families. You can have just a man and his wife. You can have a widowed mother and three children, all girls. You can have an old married couple with a son, a daughter-in-law, and two grandsons. There are thousands of possible kinds of families.

In the same way, even a few different kinds of atoms can combine into many different kinds of groups. This is why there are so many different kinds of things in the world.

When the molecules of a certain type of matter are made up of more than one kind of atom, that type of matter is known as a *compound*. There are hundreds of thousands of different compounds known to chemists. Most of the things we see are compounds or mixtures of compounds. The human body itself is made up of many thousands of different compounds.

When the molecules of a certain type of matter are made up of only one kind of atom, that type of matter is known as an *element*. Since there are 102 different kinds of atoms known, there are exactly 102 different elements.

These elements are the building blocks out of which the universe is built. From these elements the various natural processes in the earth have produced all the many compounds that exist. Nowadays chemists can manufacture almost any compound they wish if they have the necessary elements as starting materials.

Some of the 102 elements are very familiar to you. You've heard of gold, silver, copper, iron, and aluminum, surely.

Others are quite unfamiliar to any one but professional chemists. Have you ever heard of thulium, praseodymium, or gadolinium?

In this book I am going to tell you a little about every element, beginning with familiar and common ones. But first I should like to talk a little about all the elements taken together. They are often quite different from one another in appearance and behavior. Some are hard and black; some are shiny and can be beaten into different shapes; some are brittle; some are liquids under ordinary conditions; some are gases (like air) under ordinary conditions; some are colorless and others colored. The atoms of different elements have different ways of combining with one another and with the atoms of other elements. (This means that their chemical behavior is different.)

Chemists have tried to get some order out of all this variety. They have found that every atom is made up of still smaller particles. The outer portions of an atom contain a number of tiny particles called *electrons*. Each particular kind of atom has its own number of electrons. The simplest atom contains only one electron. More complicated atoms contain two, three, and so on all the way up to 102 without skipping a number. Chemists therefore give each element not only a name but also an *atomic number*. An atom that under normal conditions contains twenty-three electrons has the atomic number 23, and so on.

These electrons are arranged in layers, or shells, about the center of the atom, much like the layers of an onion. When one shell is full of electrons, the next electron goes into the next shell. Element No. 3, for instance, has its first shell (the one next to the center) full and a second shell containing one electron. Element No. 11 has its first and second shells full and a third shell containing one electron.

Element No. 19 has its first, second, and third shells full and a fourth shell containing one electron. Now the chemical behavior and appearance of elements depend a great deal on the number and arrangement of the electrons in the outermost shell. The elements numbered 3, 11, and 19 are alike in that their outermost shells contain a single electron each. For this reason they resemble one another. They are all soft metals that tarnish quickly when exposed to air. They all catch fire if dropped in water. They are all easily melted, and so on.

Chemists can arrange all the elements in such a way that elements with similar electron shell arrangements appear in the same column or, sometimes, in the same row. Such an arrangement is called a *periodic table,* and there is one on pages 16 and 17 for you to look at. The elements are listed in the order of their atomic numbers.

Elements that resemble one another because of similar electron arrangements are enclosed in a solid line and separated from one another by a dotted line. Notice that elements 3, 11, and 19, plus elements 37, 55, and 87 as well, all fall into a single column. Elements 2, 10, 18, 36, 54, and 86 find themselves in another column. As examples of similar elements that fall in the same row, notice elements 26-28 and elements 57-71. By using the periodic table, I shall often be able to discuss several similar elements at once.

At the head of each chapter you will find a small reproduction of the periodic table in which the number of each element discussed in that chapter will appear in the proper place. Other spaces in the table will be left blank. In this way you will get some idea of how the elements are related to one another.

At the end of the book the periodic table will be repeated, but with the names of the elements instead of the numbers. By then, I hope, you will be familiar with most of the names.

And now let's find out what the different elements, these building blocks of the universe, are like.

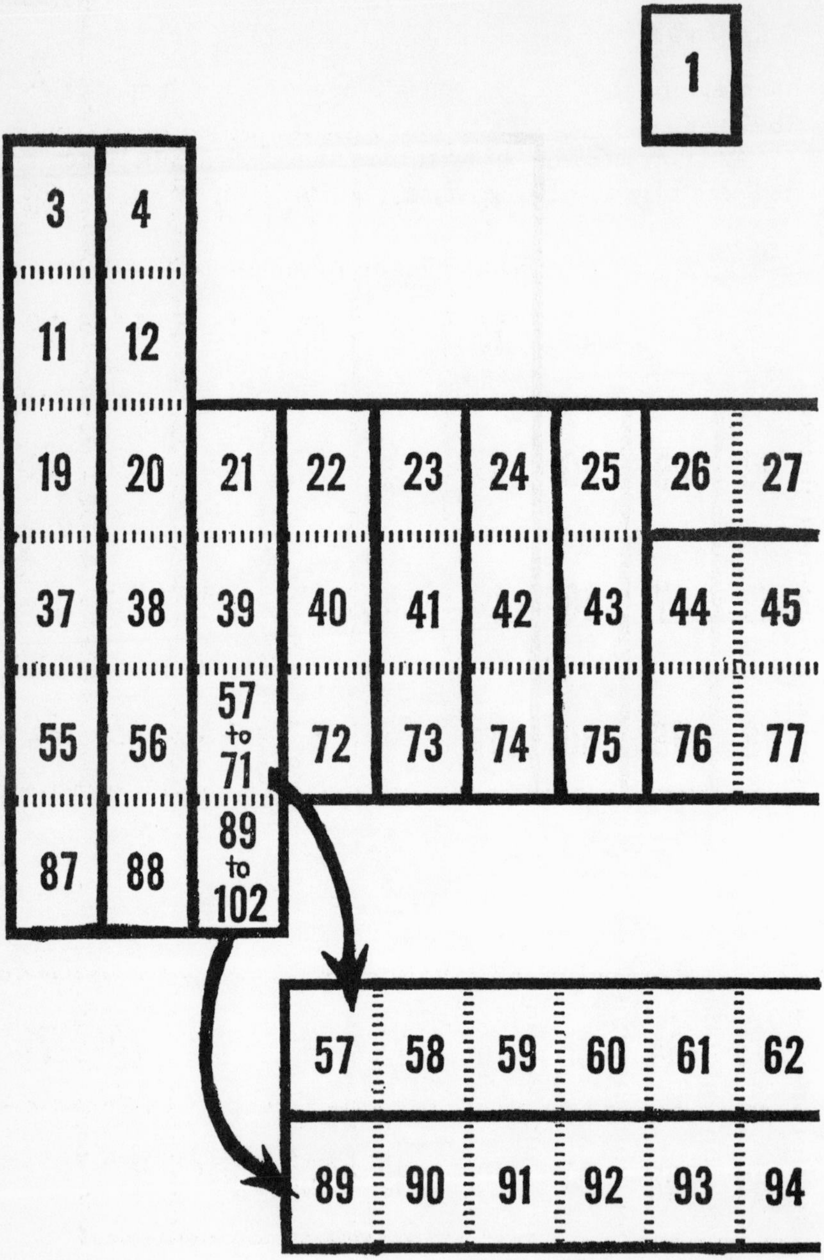
1
3
4
11
12
19
20
21
22
23
24
25
26
27
37
38
39
40
41
42
43
44
45
55
56
57 to 71
72
73
74
75
76
77
87
88
89 to 102
57
58
59
60
61
62
89
90
91
92
93
94

								2
			5	6	7	8	9	10
			13	14	15	16	17	18
28	29	30	31	32	33	34	35	36
46	47	48	49	50	51	52	53	54
78	79	80	81	82	83	84	85	86

63	64	65	66	67	68	69	70	71
95	96	97	98	99	100	101	102	

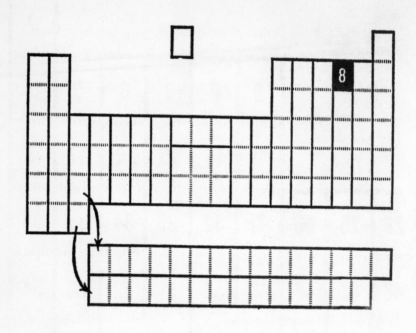

CHAPTER 1   Oxygen

THE ELEMENT WE BREATHE

THE THREE STATES

Oxygen is element No. 8. You may wonder why I begin with No. 8 rather than with No. 1. There are several reasons for that.

In the first place, oxygen is the commonest element on the earth. Nearly half of all the atoms that make up our planet are oxygen atoms. If we consider only the outermost part of the planet, the ten-mile-thick surface crust, nearly two-thirds of the atoms are oxygen atoms.

In the soil, oxygen is part of numerous compounds. That is, it is combined into molecules with various other kinds of atoms. In the air about us, however, oxygen exists as an element. One out of every five molecules in the air is made up of two oxygen atoms and nothing else. A molecule made up of two oxygen atoms is known as an *oxygen molecule*.

Oxygen is not only very common; it is also essential to life. When we breathe, we suck air into our lungs. Some of the oxygen in the air is absorbed into the body. In the body, it combines with substances obtained from the food we eat. In this way the energy that keeps the body living and working is produced.

To obtain oxygen, we must keep breathing constantly, waking or sleeping. We can live for weeks without food, if we have to, and for days without water. Five minutes without oxygen, however, will kill us.

So oxygen is a good element to begin with.

The most noticeable thing about oxygen is that it is a *gas*, and before we go any further, I must stop to explain exactly what a gas is.

Most of the things we see about us (if we are on land) are *solids*. That is, they are in a single piece that sticks together and keeps its shape if left alone. A particular solid object may be hard, like a brick, or rather soft, like a piece of wax. It may be stiff, like an iron rod; springy, like a steel spring; elastic, like a rubber ball; or crumply, like aluminum foil. Still, if you pick up one piece of it all the rest goes along; it stays in one piece.

The molecules in a solid are held together fairly tightly.

A particular molecule keeps its particular place. It may jitter about a bit (like a nervous person shifting from foot to foot while waiting), but it keeps its place.

If you heat a solid, however, the jittering of the molecules grows worse. You may reach a temperature, finally, at which they break away from one another. They are able to slip freely over and around each other. When this happens, the solid is said to *melt*. It turns into a *liquid*.

Water is the commonest and most familiar liquid, but we all know others. Alcohol is a liquid, and so are gasoline, mercury, and olive oil. Liquids don't hang together as solids do. You can't pick up a piece of water between your fingers and lift a whole glassful in that way. A quantity of liquid has no particular shape of its own; it takes the shape of any container so far as it fills it.

(Sometimes, if a molecule is rather complicated and consists of numerous atoms, a rising temperature makes it fall apart. Instead of melting, the solid is then said to *decompose*. If ordinary sugar is heated, it doesn't melt. Instead, it chars and gives off fumes. It is decomposing. Sometimes, as with dynamite, decomposition is so rapid and violent that the substance *explodes*.)

Although the molecules of liquids are not tightly bound together, they still remain close to one another. If a liquid is heated, however, there comes a time when the molecules fly away from one another altogether. They scatter and spread apart, each going its own way. When this happens, the liquid *boils*. It is turned into a *gas*.

The solid, liquid, and gaseous forms are called the *three states of matter*. Most simple compounds, and all elements, can exist in all three forms. They exist as solids, liquids, or gases, depending partly on the temperature and partly on certain other conditions of the environment.

Water is a good example of this. Ordinary water is a liquid. When water gets cold enough, however, it turns into a solid, which we call *ice*. When water gets hot enough, it turns into a gas, which we call *steam*. Ice, water, and steam are the same substance in three different states. They can be changed back and forth, one into another, by heating or cooling.

Different substances melt and boil at different temperatures. The temperature at which a particular substance melts depends on how tightly its molecules hang on to one another. The molecules in rocks, for instance, hang on to one another so tightly that they have to be heated red-hot, and even hotter, before they shake loose sufficiently to become liquid. (The lava that pours out of volcanoes in eruption is a kind of liquid rock.) The molecules in ice, on the other hand, are bound together quite weakly. Even an early spring day may be warm enough to make it melt and become water.

Some molecules hang together more weakly still. Oxygen molecules are an example of this. If the temperature were only low enough, oxygen could exist as a liquid. If it were lower still, oxygen could be a solid. No temperature that ever occurs naturally on the earth's surface is low enough, however, to keep oxygen a liquid, let alone a solid. In nature, oxygen is always a gas.

Chemists tried to create very low temperatures in the laboratory, low enough to make oxygen become a liquid. In 1877 they finally succeeded. The temperature required is about 300 degrees below zero on our ordinary Fahrenheit scale.

So, when we say that oxygen is a gas, what we really mean is that it is a gas at ordinary temperatures.

INVESTIGATING THE INVISIBLE

Gases are not easy to study. Take air, for instance, the commonest gas of all. What do you know about it? It's transparent and colorless. You can see right through it. You can't smell it or taste it. How do you even know it's there?

You know it's there because you can feel it when it moves (or when you move through it fast enough). Different parts of the air are heated to different temperatures by the sun (depending on whether the air is in the lowlands or highlands, north or south, near water or far from it). The warmer air rises while the cooler air sinks. The large air movements set up in this way are what we call *wind*. Sometimes the force of the wind is all too uncomfortable. Anyone who, like me, has lived through several hurricanes can testify to that. Air exists, all right.

It may not seem to you that air weighs anything. We move about in it easily, without any feeling of being loaded down. Still, gases are matter, just as solids and liquids are. They do have weight.

To be sure, gases weigh less than solids and liquids. A quart of water weighs about two pounds. A quart of air, under ordinary conditions, weighs only 1/20 ounce. Even that can add up in larger amounts. The air in an ordinary living room, say twelve feet wide and eighteen feet long and eight feet high, weighs 150 pounds.

We are, in fact, at the bottom of a layer of air stretching for miles and miles above us. There is enough of it so that fifteen pounds of air rests on every square inch of our body's surface. But the air fills us and presses equally in all directions; so it balances out, and we don't feel the weight.

How can you tell two different gases apart? Suppose a chemist places two bottles in front of you and tells you that one bottle contains air, the other oxygen. The bottles look quite the same to you; both look empty. The gases they hold are colorless, odorless, tasteless. The oxygen is a trifle heavier than the air, to be sure, but not enough so that you can tell the difference easily.

What you do, then, is to compare the way in which the two gases behave under similar conditions. Take a thin sliver of wood, and set one end on fire. After it has burnt a moment or two, blow the flame out so that the lighted end is merely smoldering. Dip the smoldering tip of the wood into the bottle of air. It continues to smolder, and after a while it goes out. Now dip the smoldering tip into the bottle of oxygen. Instantly it bursts into flame, and it continues to burn more brightly than it did when first lighted.

Why is this?

Oxygen is an *active* substance; its molecules combine easily with those of other substances. When wood, for instance, is heated, it decomposes and gives off gases. These gases catch fire; that is, they begin combining with oxygen molecules in the air. In doing so, they produce energy, and this energy makes itself felt as heat and seen as light.

If the flame that results is blown out, there is not enough oxygen in the air to keep the smoldering spark going, unless the wood is heated again; so the spark goes out. If the smoldering wood is again placed in pure oxygen, however, it will combine with the oxygen so fast that it will become hot enough to burst into flame again. (There has to be at least a spark, however. Wood in which there is no spark at all won't burst into flame even in pure oxygen.)

Since oxygen encourages things to catch fire, it is said to support *combustion*, or burning. It is the oxygen in air that enables wood, paper, gasoline, and many other things to burn when they are heated. If the oxygen were removed from air, what was left would not support combustion. A lighted candle or a piece of burning wood inserted into what was left of air after the oxygen has been removed would go out at once.

Under ordinary conditions, substances that burn do not do so until heated to a certain *ignition temperature*. Below these temperatures, combination with oxygen goes on very slowly. Heat is slowly formed as combination proceeds. This heat lingers and collects in substances that don't transmit heat to the air easily. Oily rags are the best example of this. As the heat accumulates over the days and weeks, the ignition temperature is finally reached and the rags burst into flame. This is called *spontaneous combustion*, since the fire seems to start spontaneously (that is, all by itself). Spontaneous combustion has burnt down many a house.

Your life depends on a kind of slow combustion, within the body, of the foods you eat. It is this combustion that keeps your body warm and gives you the energy to do all the things you do. Without oxygen to support combustion your life could not go on for even five minutes. Air supports life because a part of it is oxygen. If you were to breathe air from which the oxygen has been removed, you would quickly suffocate and die. You consume over 20 quarts of oxygen each hour if resting, considerably more if you're working or exercising.

Even fish and other sea life can't live without oxygen. They "breathe water," it is true; but small quantities of oxygen are dissolved in the water, and fishes' gills remove oxygen from the water and pass it into their blood just as your lungs remove oxygen from the air and pass it into your blood. If all the oxygen were removed from water, a fish would drown as quickly as a man.

People sometimes have illnesses that make it hard for their lungs to take oxygen from the air. Such people are often given pure oxygen to breathe. The oxygen is led into a plastic hood, called an *oxygen tent*, that fits over the head and chest. People who have heart attacks are also sometimes put into oxygen tents. More oxygen gets into the blood then, and the heart, which pumps the blood to all parts of the body, does not have to work so hard. After his heart attack in September 1955, President Eisenhower was placed in an oxygen tent for several days.

SEPARATING AIR

Pure oxygen is stored in strong metal tanks of various sizes (some standing as tall as a man). The stored oxygen is under pressure; that is, its molecules are squeezed together so that more of it can be pushed into the tank. When a tank is full, it holds 135 times as much oxygen as it would if the gas weren't under pressure. If its nozzle were opened wide, the oxygen would rush out with extreme force, as though from a rocket exhaust. Tanks must therefore be fitted with special devices that let the gas out slowly.

One must also be careful to have no flame or sparks or especially inflammable objects about when pure oxygen is being used. The oxygen won't burn or explode itself, but it will make other things burn furiously.

Where does the pure oxygen that fills our tanks come from?

One way of getting oxygen is to take oxygen atoms from a compound in which they are held rather loosely. When such a compound is heated, the oxygen atoms break loose, form oxygen molecules, and collect as oxygen gas. The oxygen can be led through a tube into a container of water.

The incoming oxygen forces the water out, and what is left is a container of oxygen.

In 1772 a Swedish chemist named Karl Scheele, and in 1774 a British chemist named Joseph Priestley, both discovered oxygen in just this way. They both realized that the gas they had obtained was different from air. Scheele called it *fire air*.

A year or two later a French chemist, Antoine Lavoisier, first called the gas oxygen. He called it that from Greek words meaning "giving rise to sourness." He used that name because he thought oxygen occurred in the molecules of certain compounds known as acids, which generally have a sour taste. Lavoisier was wrong. Acids may contain oxygen, or they may not. Oxygen has nothing to do with sourness. But the name stuck.

Heating a compound in order to break up its molecules is all right as far as it goes, but we get only small amounts of oxygen that way. To get a great deal of oxygen, we use *liquid air*.

Air can be turned into a liquid if the temperature is made low enough. When liquid air boils, it turns into a gas again, just as water, when it boils, turns into a gas (steam).

Air contains more than one kind of molecule. One-fifth of it is oxygen. The rest is mostly another kind of gas altogether, called nitrogen. Liquid oxygen boils and becomes a gas at a very low temperature but liquid nitrogen boils and becomes a gas at a temperature lower still. If liquid air, which is a mixture of both, is allowed to warm up slowly, the nitrogen boils and bubbles away faster than the oxygen does.

This process can actually be seen. Liquid nitrogen is colorless like water. Liquid oxygen is blue. If liquid air is allowed to stand and slowly boil, it turns bluer as the liquid nitrogen vanishes and what is left becomes more and more liquid oxygen.

By taking advantage of this difference in boiling temperature between nitrogen and oxygen, we *fractionate* liquid air. That is, we separate it into a fraction that is oxygen and a fraction that is nitrogen. Both can be stored in tanks and put to use.

Oxygen is used in medicine not only for oxygen tents but also for mixing with anesthetics. A patient who is getting his anesthetic through the lungs breathes ether (or some other anesthetic) mixed with oxygen.

In industry oxygen is fed into a stream of inflammable gas to create a very hot flame that can be used for welding and for cutting steel.

Liquefying oxygen is one way of squeezing a lot of oxygen into a comparatively small space. Liquid oxygen is used to burn the fuel in modern missiles and rockets. Missile-men refer to liquid oxygen by the abbreviation LOX.

OXYGEN AND A HALF

The oxygen molecule, as I said above, consists of two oxygen atoms. Sometimes three oxygen atoms get together and form a molecule. A collection of such three-atom molecules is one and a half times as heavy as ordinary oxygen. The three-atom molecule is still oxygen, but it behaves differently from the ordinary two-atom molecules—so differently, in fact, that chemists have given it a name of its own. They call it *ozone*.

You may have heard the word "ozone" used as a slangy expression for very fresh air in the country, especially in the mountains. Perhaps you have an idea that ozone, with three oxygen atoms in its molecule, is one and a half times as good as ordinary oxygen. All this is quite wrong. There is practically no ozone in ordinary air, even in the mountains; and, if there were, you wouldn't like it. It has a strong, sharp odor (the word "ozone" comes from a Greek word meaning "I smell") and it is poisonous.

The third oxygen atom doesn't get into the molecule easily. It doesn't fit well and has to be pushed. Energy to do the pushing has to be supplied. A supply of such energy can come from high-tension electricity. Some of the oxygen in the neighborhood of certain kinds of electrical apparatus is changed to ozone. The ozone can be smelled easily enough. Another source of energy is ultraviolet rays, the kind that comes from mercury-vapor lamps or from "sun lamps." Ozone can sometimes be smelled near such lamps.

Sunlight is rich in ultraviolet rays. When sunlight hits the upper atmosphere, some of the oxygen there is converted to ozone. This thin *ozone layer*, some fifteen miles up in the air, absorbs much of the ultraviolet of the sun and prevents it from reaching the surface of the earth. This is fortunate for us, since otherwise the amount of ultraviolet striking us would be fatal. The ozone layer is necessary to life.

It is hard, as we have seen, for the third oxygen atom to get into the oxygen molecule, but it is easy for it to get out again. Ozone is always changing back into ordinary oxygen, releasing an oxygen atom as it does so. Ozone is *unstable*. The oxygen atom that is released is ready to attach itself to something else. In this way, ozone brings about chemical changes even more easily than ordinary oxygen does; it is more active than oxygen. In fact, there have been thoughts of using liquid ozone instead of liquid oxygen in missiles, but the instability of the substance makes it very hard to handle.

Mercury and silver aren't affected by ordinary oxygen. They will tarnish, however, in the presence of ozone. The molecules of certain colored substances are changed by ozone into molecules that are colorless; that is, ozone acts as a *bleach.*

Ozone is also a *deodorant;* it will change the molecules of some odorous substances into molecules that have no odor. If small electrical devices that change oxygen into ozone are placed in industrial refrigerators, for example, the ozone that is produced will deodorize its surroundings as it changes back into oxygen.

Ozone has still another use. It is an ideal substance with which to purify a city's water supply. Small quantities of it are mixed with air and are then bubbled through the water. Germs are killed and chemical impurities are often destroyed, too. As always, the ozone changes to oxygen and leaves no trace.

When an element exists in two or more different forms, these are spoken of as *allotropes.* Ozone is an allotrope of oxygen. Ozone differs from oxygen even in appearance. It is not colorless but has a definite bluish tinge. Liquid ozone is a very dark blue, almost black. We shall come across more interesting allotropes soon.

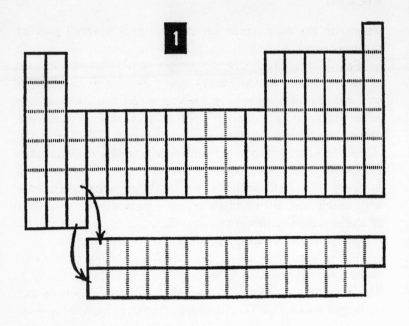

CHAPTER 2 **Hydrogen**

THE LIGHTEST ELEMENT

THE GAS EARTH LOST

The simplest substance of all is hydrogen. It is element No. 1. The hydrogen atom is the smallest, lightest, and least complicated of all the atoms known. It may be for this reason that hydrogen is the commonest substance, by far, in all the universe. (Oxygen is the commonest substance on the earth, but the earth is only a small part of the universe.)

People who study the stars now think that 90 percent of all the atoms in the universe are hydrogen atoms. Our sun, for instance, is mostly hydrogen. So are most of the other stars. So is the very fine material that is scattered among the stars.

On the earth, however, hydrogen is not very common. Of the atoms in the earth's outermost layers only 3 percent are hydrogen. In the earth's interior the percentage is probably much less. Yet at first the earth must have been made of the same substances as the rest of the universe. What happened to the hydrogen, then?

The explanation is in the smallness of the hydrogen atom. Like oxygen atoms, hydrogen atoms team up in pairs. The resulting combination of two hydrogen atoms is the *hydrogen molecule.* The hydrogen molecule is smaller than any other molecule known. It is even smaller than a single atom of any other substance.

All molecules are continually in motion. The molecules in a solid are fixed in place, but they vibrate continuously; the molecules in a liquid move more freely; and those in a gas move more freely still.

At ordinary temperatures the oxygen molecules in the air are moving at a speed of over four miles a minute. They are, of course, continually colliding with one another and bouncing off. The higher the temperature, the faster the molecules move; they speed up, for example, in the air surrounding a furnace.

Small molecules move faster than large ones. At ordinary temperatures the hydrogen molecule moves at just about seven miles a minute. (This is the average speed. Some particular molecules may be moving a bit faster, some a bit slower.)

An object that moves fast enough can escape from the earth altogether. If you throw a stone into the air, it reaches a certain height, and then the earth's gravity pulls it back. If you throw it harder, it reaches a greater height before falling back. If you fire a cannon into the air, the shell may climb many miles before falling back. If you can make something take off fast enough, it will not fall back at all. The speed at which this happens is called the *escape velocity*.

Hydrogen molecules move at speeds that are near the escape velocity. For that reason, if there were any hydrogen molecules in the atmosphere, they would move away from the earth and leak out into space. The earth, when it was young, may have been hotter than it is now, perhaps much hotter. The hydrogen molecules would then have moved all the faster and leaked away all the more quickly.

So there is practically no hydrogen left in the atmosphere today. The little hydrogen that we find on the earth is still there because it was tied up in molecules containing heavier atoms.

Oxygen molecules are sixteen times as heavy as hydrogen molecules and move more slowly, nowhere near the escape velocity. Oxygen, therefore, does not leak away; it remains in the atmosphere.

Some planets are larger and heavier than the earth and therefore have a greater pull of gravity; on such planets a molecule would have to move even faster in order to escape. On the planet Jupiter, whose gravity is two and a half times as great as the earth's, and where hydrogen molecules move more slowly than they do here because Jupiter *is* colder than the earth, even hydrogen molecules do not move fast enough to escape. Jupiter therefore has a great deal of hydrogen in its atmosphere. So do the other large outer planets—Saturn, Uranus, and Neptune.

A planet that is smaller than the earth cannot even do as well as our planet can. Mars, for instance, has a gravity only two-fifths as great as the earth's. Most of its atmosphere has leaked away, and what is left is very thin. Our moon, which is smaller still, and has a gravity only one-sixth as great as the earth's, has no atmosphere at all.

Although there is little hydrogen in the earth's solid crust, two out of every three atoms in the oceans are hydrogen. Earth's gravity has retained hydrogen to that extent anyway. Since hydrogen is one of the elements essential to living tissue (three-fifths of the atoms in our bodies are hydrogen) this is fortunate.

FLOATING ON HIGH

At ordinary temperatures, hydrogen, like oxygen, is a gas. It remains a gas even at temperatures that cause oxygen to become a liquid. Eventually, at temperatures lower still, hydrogen becomes first a liquid and then a solid.

Hydrogen gas is the lightest substance known. In Chapter 1, I said that the air in an ordinary living room weighs 150 pounds. If such a room were filled with hydrogen instead of air, the hydrogen would weigh only ten pounds.

In the same way, liquid hydrogen is the lightest liquid known and solid hydrogen is the lightest solid known. A quart of water, for instance, weighs two pounds. A quart of liquid hydrogen weighs only two and a quarter ounces.

The lightness of hydrogen is one of the most dramatic

things about it. Wood rises in water because wood is lighter than water. In the same way, something that is lighter than air, as hydrogen is, rises in air. If a light bag is filled with hydrogen and released, it rises into the air. If weights are hung from the bottom, they move up with the bag. The larger the bag of hydrogen, the more weight it will carry. A large enough bag will carry a man.

Since air gets thinner and lighter as one travels upward, the hydrogen-filled bag rises more and more slowly the higher it goes. Finally it comes to a standstill. If a weight is dropped from it, it rises some more. If some of the hydrogen is let out of the bag, it slowly descends. A gas-filled bag that can be made to rise and hover and sink in this fashion is called a *balloon*.

Balloons are by no means a recent invention. The first balloons large enough to carry men were built in 1783 in France by two brothers named Joseph and Jacques Mont-golfier. These did not use hydrogen, but heated air, which is lighter than cool air. The use of hydrogen, however, came in only a few months afterward.

Ordinary balloons float helplessly in the air, at the mercy of the wind, just as a chip of wood floats helplessly on the water, at the mercy of the current. If a balloon is large enough to carry gasoline and motor-driven propellors, it can be made to move through the air at will, much as a motorboat is driven over water. Such a motor-driven balloon is called a *dirigible balloon* (that is, one that can be direc-ted) or simply a dirigible.

The first successful dirigible was built in 1900 in Ger-many by Count Ferdinand von Zeppelin. Instead of using just a bag of silk or other textile material, he built an alu-minum framework shaped like a fat cigar and put the hydro-gen bags inside that.

Until the 1930s there was great interest in these cigar-shaped dirigibles. The United States, Great Britain, France, Italy, and, especially, Germany built about 150 of them altogether. The larger ones were longer than the Empire State Building is tall. They carried, underneath, cabins that looked small in comparison but were large enough, sometimes, to hold a hundred or more people. The most successful dirigible, the *Graf Zeppelin* (named after the inventor), was German-built and made many trips across the Atlantic Ocean as well as a trip around the world.

The largest dirigible of all, the German-built *Hindenburg*, was destroyed by the hydrogen that filled its bag. Hydrogen, it turned out, was a dangerous gas to have around. Let's see why.

BEWARE OF THE SPARK

Hydrogen is a fairly active element. Hydrogen molecules will combine with oxygen molecules and, in so doing, release energy. This energy appears mostly in the form of heat, a little in the form of light. In other words, hydrogen will burn in oxygen (or in air), giving a hot, pale-blue flame.

Some of you have seen such a flame, since the cooking gas used in many houses contains hydrogen. Cooking is one example of the good use to which the heat of burning hydrogen can be put.

In industry, special hydrogen flames are used. Pure hydrogen (from a metal cylinder containing the gas under pressure) is led through one pipe, and pure oxygen through another. The openings of the two pipes are close together so that, as the two gases come out, they mix. If a match is put to the mixture, an exceedingly hot flame is formed. This is called an *oxyhydrogen torch*. The flame is hot enough to cut through steel as if it were butter. Perhaps you've seen such torches in operation on construction jobs. The operators of such torches have to wear special masks and protective clothing because the red-hot metal casts a blinding glow and often a shower of sparks.

The fuel used in missiles is often some hydrogen-containing substance such as kerosene or alcohol, which combines violently with liquid oxygen to produce the necessary thrust. Liquid hydrogen, itself, would be more efficient, but hydrogen liquefies at such a low temperature that keeping it liquid during the countdown poses quite a problem.

It's all very well to have hydrogen flames when you want them, but sometimes hydrogen burns when you don't want it to—for instance, when you have a tremendous quantity of it inside a dirigible. There is always a chance that a small leak in the bag may let some hydrogen escape into the cabin underneath. This hydrogen can easily catch fire and then set fire to the bag above. Mixtures of hydrogen and oxygen will, in fact, explode with great violence. A mixture of two parts of hydrogen and one of oxygen is called *detonating gas* for this reason.

For this reason, until a substitute for hydrogen was used (see Chapter 4), there were always strict rules about fire on dirigibles. No smoking was allowed, of course, and no fire or spark of any kind. Even nails in the shoe soles were forbidden because they might strike a spark against the floor.

Just the same, on May 6, 1937, as the giant dirigible *Hindenburg* was maneuvering for a landing at Lakehurst, New Jersey, some spark did flare despite all the precautions. In a second the dirigible was a mass of flames. It was the final blow to the dirigible as a practical type of vehicle. No large ones have been built since or are likely to be built. Airplanes have taken over completely.

Fire is bad enough, but that's not the only danger involved in the use of hydrogen. As long as hydrogen is fed into air or oxygen a little at a time, a manageable flame results. Suppose, however, that hydrogen and oxygen are well mixed. Nothing happens under ordinary conditions. But what if a little spark raises the temperature of just a small bit of that hydrogen-oxygen mixture? The hydrogen and oxygen molecules in that little bit combine. The energy they produce is enough to make the neighboring molecules combine, and these set off the molecules near them. In a tiny fraction of a second all the molecules have combined and released energy in one big wallop. This is called an *explosion*.

Any inflammable substance in the form of a gas, a liquid, or a fine dust can explode when mixed with air. The commonest such substance in the house is cooking gas. This often has hydrogen in it or other substances that are almost as dangerous. If the gas jet is opened and allowed to remain open for a few moments before the match is applied, you may notice that there is a small pop before the gas settles down to quiet burning.

If the gas is allowed to flow for a while (because of a leak, for instance), it may slowly mix with the air in the room. Then, when the pilot light or someone's match or cigarette finally sets the mixture off, the explosion may wreck the house and kill people. If you suspect there may be a gas leak, don't ever look for it with a match.

For the same reason, don't look for a leak in the gasoline tank of your car with a match, and don't smoke while you're using an inflammable dry cleaner.

One use to which hydrogen is put has nothing to do with its lightness or its ability to burn. This is its use in the improvement of plant oils.

The oil obtained from cotton seeds is cheap, and large quantities of it can be produced; but, unlike butter, lard, and olive oil, it cannot be used in cooking. Cottonseed oil has a definite and rather unpleasant taste. The cottonseed oil molecule contains a lot of hydrogen atoms (over fifty), but there is room for several extra hydrogen atoms to be squeezed in. If the oil is mixed with hydrogen under the proper conditions, the molecules pick up those extra hydrogen atoms. The new molecules, with all the hydrogen they can hold, now form a solid fat. This fat is white, odorless, and tasteless and keeps very well. The original cottonseed oil has become quite suitable for use in cooking.

This process is known as *hydrogenation*. Kitchen fats such as Crisco and Spry are examples of hydrogenated cottonseed oil.

FIRE INTO WATER

The way hydrogen has of burning was the first thing chemists noticed about it. Hydrogen was first collected and really studied by a British chemist, Henry Cavendish, in 1766, and he called it *inflammable air*. Its modern name, however, was given it some years later by the same Lavoisier who named oxygen. He called the new gas hydrogen from Greek words meaning "giving rise to water."

This is a very good name, for that is exactly what hydrogen does when it burns. It gives rise to water. If you hold a cold piece of glass or porcelain over a small hydrogen flame, you will notice that drops of liquid collect. If a chemist studied this liquid, he would find it to be pure water.

When hydrogen molecules combine with oxygen molecules, they form new molecules, containing two hydrogen atoms and one oxygen atom apiece. Such a molecule is the *water molecule.* All the water you've ever seen, all the oceans, lakes, rivers, rain (and snow and ice, for that matter, and steam, too) consist of these three-atom molecules, made of two hydrogens and one oxygen.

Although water is so common that we take it very much for granted, it is really a remarkable substance. Books can be written (and have been) about the many ways in which it makes life possible. You can get an idea of its importance from the fact that about 60 percent of the weight of a human being is water.

It is because of all these water molecules that there are more hydrogen atoms in the human body than all other kinds of atoms put together.

Since hydrogen and oxygen combine to form water, the water molecule can be split apart into hydrogen and oxygen. We do this by dipping wires into the water and passing an electric current along the wires and through the water under the proper conditions. Oxygen gas collects around one wire and hydrogen gas around the other. The wires are called *electrodes,* and this process of water-splitting is called *electrolysis.*

It is by electrolyzing water in this way that industry gets its supply of hydrogen. Next to fractionating liquid air, electrolyzing water is the most important way of getting oxygen, too.

An older way of getting hydrogen was to take it from compounds called acids, which I mentioned in the previous chapter. All acids contain hydrogen atoms that are held somewhat loosely. The more loosely the hydrogen atoms are held, the stronger the acid. If certain metals are placed in an acid, the acid combines with the metal and lets go of the hydrogen atoms. The atoms thus set free combine to form hydrogen molecules and collect as hydrogen gas. The storage batteries in automobiles contain an acid and a metal, and at certain times hydrogen gas can collect. People who used a match to see the water level in a battery have sometimes been injured by the explosion that followed.

WATER'S UNSTABLE RELATION

Water is not the only compound that can be formed of hydrogen and oxygen atoms. Just as an extra oxygen atom can be added to ordinary oxygen to form the unstable, active ozone, so an extra oxygen atom can be added to water to form the unstable active *hydrogen peroxide*.

The hydrogen peroxide molecule contains two hydrogen atoms and two oxygen atoms. Hydrogen peroxide is similar to ozone in some ways because it, too, releases that extra oxygen as fast as it can. Like ozone, hydrogen peroxide is a bleach or a bacteria-killer. Hydrogen peroxide is so active that it has been used in the chemical mixtures that have powered rockets and torpedoes.

Hydrogen peroxide is mixed with water to make it safer to use. The hydrogen peroxide you buy in a drugstore is 3 percent hydrogen peroxide and 97 percent water. You are not being cheated, however. If it were stronger, it would be too strong to use.

Light and heat make hydrogen peroxide break down to ordinary water faster. For that reason the drugstore sells you hydrogen peroxide in a dark-brown or dark-blue bottle to keep out the light, and the label tells you to store it in a cool place.

Hydrogen peroxide is sometimes put on cuts in order to kill bacteria and cut down the danger of infection. A substance in blood causes hydrogen peroxide to break down very fast. Perhaps you have noticed that hydrogen peroxide on a cut will foam and turn into a white lather. That foaming is caused by the oxygen gas being formed as the hydrogen peroxide breaks down with great rapidity.

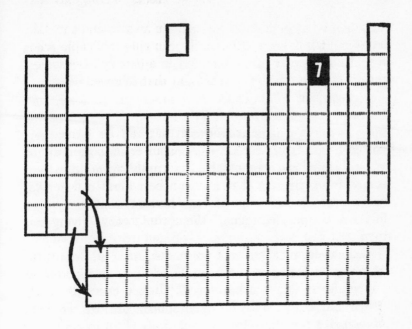

CHAPTER 3 Nitrogen

THE "LIFELESS" ELEMENT

THE SUFFOCATING PART OF AIR

In Chapter 1, I said that oxygen forms only one-fifth of the air. Almost all the rest is nitrogen, which is element No. 7.

In the 1770s, when chemists were discovering oxygen, they also discovered, of course, the other gas of the air. This other gas would not support combustion. A candle burning in a closed vessel used up about a fifth of the air

41

and then went out. When the oxygen was gone, what was left would not keep the candle burning. This other gas would not support life, either. Mice put into closed vessels suffocated and died as soon as most of the oxygen was gone.

Scheele, in 1772, called this other gas *foul air*, and Lavoisier called it *azote*, from Greek words meaning "no life." Lavoisier's name is still used in the French language, and in English, too, certain compounds containing nitrogen are still called azo compounds. The English name "nitrogen" comes from the fact that a common mineral called *niter* (now oftener called saltpeter) was found to contain nitrogen in its molecule. "Nitrogen," therefore, means "giving rise to niter."

Mind you, nitrogen isn't poisonous. After all, four-fifths of the air is nitrogen. We breathe it in and out constantly, and under ordinary conditions it doesn't harm us at all. We would die in pure nitrogen simply because we need oxygen. It's not the nitrogen, but the lack of oxygen, that would kill us. (The same, by the way, is true of hydrogen, which is also suffocating but not poisonous.)

There is one time when nitrogen can harm us. Nitrogen dissolves in water and in fatty substances to a small extent. (So do oxygen and hydrogen.) Some of the nitrogen that gets into our body through the lungs dissolves in our blood and tissues. That's all right. It does no harm and doesn't even get in the way of anything.

When nitrogen is put under pressure, however, more of it dissolves. This actually happens when people are working in diving bells under water, as when tunnels are being built under rivers. The air pressure has to be increased to keep the water out. The bodies of such people are loaded with extra nitrogen. While the gas is in solution, though, it still does no harm.

But suppose a person is brought up from beneath the river, and the pressure of the air is allowed to return to normal quickly. His blood and tissues can't hold all that nitrogen any longer. Nitrogen comes bubbling out in his joints and blood vessels and elsewhere. The effects are extremely painful and can be fatal. The condition is known as the *bends*.

For this reason, people who have been working under pressure are restored to normal gradually in *decompression chambers*. In this way, the extra nitrogen is gotten rid of little by little.

THE USEFULNESS OF DOING NOTHING

The *nitrogen molecule* is made up of two nitrogen atoms. This should remind you of oxygen and hydrogen. There is one important difference, though. The nitrogen atoms hold each other more tightly than the oxygen or hydrogen atoms do in their molecules. The nitrogen atoms hold each other so tightly, in fact, that they seldom let go long enough to combine with other types of atoms or molecules.

As a result, the nitrogen molecule is standoffish, aloof, so to speak. It doesn't react with most other substances except under unusual circumstances. It won't burn in oxygen. Nothing will burn in it, or almost nothing. Chemists speak of nitrogen as being an *inert* element.

The fact that nitrogen is inert doesn't mean that it is useless, not by any means. There are times when inertness is exactly what is wanted.

A light bulb, for instance, contains a thin metal wire that gets white-hot when an electric current passes through it. If the bulb were full of air, the white-hot metal would combine with the oxygen and burn out almost at once. At first, therefore, light bulbs had all the air drawn out of them. They contained nothing, not even a gas. Such a state of complete nothingness is called a *vacuum*. But a vacuum wasn't quite satisfactory, either. It is easier for atoms of metal to evaporate away in a vacuum. The white-hot wire would gradually grow thinner and then break. So the bulbs were filled with nitrogen, which could be obtained in quantity from liquid air. The gas slowed down the evaporation of the metal wire, and, since it was inert, it wouldn't combine with the metal. Light bulbs lasted much longer thereafter.

Sometimes, when metals are being welded at high temperatures, there is trouble because the hot metal combines with the oxygen in the air. Since the oxyhydrogen torch needs no air in order to burn (it carries its own supply of oxygen, as we saw in Chapter 2), the metal to be welded can be protected from the air by a continuous stream of nitrogen. The metal then remains uncombined, even at high temperatures, and the welding process goes along perfectly.

PUTTING NITROGEN TO WORK

Although nitrogen gas is useless to life, certain compounds containing nitrogen are absolutely necessary for life. The most important substances in our bodies (and in all other forms of life) contain nitrogen.

Where does this nitrogen come from? We can't get it from the air, nor can other animals or plants. The nitrogen we breathe can't be used. The answer is that we get the nitrogen from substances in the food we eat. Some of our food probably consists of meat from other animals, and that meat contains nitrogen. Where did those animals get their nitrogen? They got it by eating plants or by eating other animals that had eaten plants. All the nitrogen that we and other animals have in our bodies, if we trace it back far enough, comes from plants.

And where do plants get their nitrogen? They get it from certain compounds in the soil that contain nitrogen atoms within their molecules. These compounds are called *nitrates*. The saltpeter (niter) I mentioned at the beginning of the chapter is a nitrate.

After a plant or animal dies, it decays, and much of the nitrogen it contains is restored to the soil in a form that plants can use. In this way, the soil is kept fertile. Animal wastes such as manure also contain nitrogen in a form that plants can use. Manure is therefore a *fertilizer;* in primitive farming, in fact, it is a very valuable product of the barns and stables and is carefully preserved.

This passage of useful nitrogen compounds from soil to plant to animal and back to the soil is called the *nitrogen cycle*. There are two places, however, where the cycle, as described here, leaks. First, when a dead body decays or when animal wastes are allowed to stand, some of the nitrogen atoms in the compounds break loose; they become nitrogen molecules and escape into the air, where they can no longer be used. Second, the nitrates in the soil, being soluble in water, dissolve gradually in rainwater and are washed out to sea.

If these leaks were not balanced by new supplies of nitrogen, life on land would eventually come to an end. Somehow, nitrogen-containing compounds must be entering the soil. The only place from which such compounds can get their new nitrogen is the air, but how?

The thunderstorm is one answer. Every time there is a flash of lightning, the nitrogen in the neighborhood of the flash is forced to combine with oxygen. The energy of the lightning bolt is enough to do this difficult job. The nitrogen-oxygen compound dissolves in the rainwater to form a compound known as *nitric acid*. Its molecule contains an atom of nitrogen, one of hydrogen and three of oxygen. When nitric acid hits the soil, it is converted to nitrate.

Nitric acid is one of the strong acids and very dangerous to skin and eyes if handled carelessly, but the amount of nitric acid in one raindrop is so tiny that it can almost be ignored. Still, a great number of raindrops fall all over the earth each day. It is estimated that 250,000 tons of nitric acid are deposited on the earth each day by thunderstorms.

That sounds like a lot, but, spread over the entire earth, it isn't really. It's not enough to keep the nitrogen cycle going at sufficient speed. Fortunately, there is still another, and more important, answer. Bacteria!

Certain bacteria living in the soil are actually capable of using the nitrogen molecules of the air. No other kind of living thing can do this. These bacteria combine the nitrogen with other kinds of atoms to form compounds that plants can use. These bacteria live preferably in little lumps or swellings on the roots of certain plants, such as peas, beans, clover, alfalfa, and peanuts. It has been estimated that over 40 pounds of gaseous nitrogen are made into compounds each year by the bacteria in one acre of soil.

Even the ancient Romans knew that, if plants such as these were grown and then plowed under, the fertility of the soil would be increased. Other plants would grow better the next year. Indeed, all living things owe a great debt to these tiny soil bacteria.

IN WAR AND PEACE

As I have said, it is hard to get nitrogen to combine with

other elements to form compounds. Such compounds, once they are formed, are often easy to break apart. *Ammonium nitrate* is an example of this. It contains two nitrogen atoms, four hydrogen atoms and three oxygen atoms in its molecule. Under ordinary conditions it seems harmless enough—just a white, salt-like substance.

If heated, though, the molecule of ammonium nitrate breaks apart, giving off a lot of energy. The energy is enough to cause neighboring molecules to break down, and they set off still others. In no time at all the entire quantity of ammonium nitrate goes off with a tremendous bang. Ammonium nitrate is an *explosive*. Note the difference between ammonium nitrate and hydrogen. Hydrogen will explode when mixed with oxygen; keep oxygen away, and you can do anything you want with hydrogen. Ammonium nitrate, however, needs no help. It can explode all by itself.

In 1947, in fact, in the harbor of Texas City, Texas, a shipload of ammonium nitrate blew up and wrecked the town as disastrously as if a squadron of airplanes had bombed it.

Some other important explosives are *nitrocellulose, nitroglycerine,* and *trinitrotoluene.* Note the "nitro" in each name; this shows that the molecule contains nitrogen atoms. Perhaps you know trinitrotoluene better by its initials, *TNT.*

Explosives are used in peacetime to blast away obstructions in road-building, in mining, and so on. They are used to a much greater extent, of course, in wartime. One of the most important tasks facing a nation at war is making sure it has an ample supply of explosives.

Among the important raw materials necessary for the making of explosives are nitrates, which are used as the source of nitrogen. Before World War I, the chief source of nitrates was a dry desert in northern Chile. Nitrates had accumulated there when certain prehistoric lakes had dried up, and there was never enough rainfall afterward to wash the nitrates away.

After World War I began, however, Great Britain controlled the seas, and Germany couldn't get nitrate-carrying ships from Chile through the blockade. As the war progressed, the Germans began to run short of ammunition. This must have been very frustrating for them, for there was all the nitrogen anyone could want in the air all about them and yet that nitrogen was useless.

A German chemist, named Fritz Haber, discovered a way out. He found that nitrogen could be made to combine with hydrogen if the gases were mixed properly and heated quite hot and put under a lot of pressure, provided certain metals were added to the mixture. When conditions were just right, molecules containing one atom of nitrogen and three of hydrogen were formed. This nitrogen-hydrogen compound is *ammonia*.

Once ammonia was obtained, the problem was solved. Ammonia could be easily changed into nitrates, and those could be easily changed into explosives. Now Germany had all the explosives it needed. It fought on for two more years and almost won World War I. If it had not been for the *Haber process*, Germany would probably have been forced to surrender in 1916.

The Haber process, of course, can be put to good use in peacetime. In the United States alone some 300,000 tons of ammonia a year are manufactured out of nitrogen from air and hydrogen from water. This ammonia can be converted not only to explosives, but also to fertilizer. Modern farmers can now use clean chemical fertilizers and need not depend on animal waste.

(Incidentally, Germany did not turn out to be at all grateful to Haber. When the Nazis came to power in 1933, Haber was forced out of his job and out of the country, because it happened that he was Jewish.)

A GAS WITH AN ODOR

Ammonia, which I have just mentioned, is a familiar household chemical. At ordinary temperatures it is a light gas (only half as heavy as air), but it is usually met with dissolved in water to form *ammonia water* which is also called *spirits of ammonia*. This is used in the household to clean glass surfaces.

Unlike hydrogen, oxygen, and nitrogen, ammonia has an odor. The odor is penetrating, pungent, and quite unpleasant and choking. The ordinary ammonia water used in the home is weak enough not to be too dangerous. The stronger solutions used in chemical laboratories must be handled carefully and with good ventilation.

This trick ammonia has of dissolving in water is unusual in one way. No gas dissolves in water quite as easily as ammonia does. In Chapter 1, you may remember, I said that oxygen dissolves slightly in water and that fish live on this dissolved oxygen. Actually, a quart of cold water dissolves only three cubic inches of oxygen. As for nitrogen and hydrogen, the quart of water would dissolve only one and a half cubic inches of either. That same quart of water, however, will dissolve 60,000 cubic inches of ammonia. We shall come across other soluble gases in this book, but no others quite so soluble as that.

Unlike oxygen, hydrogen, and nitrogen, ammonia can be made liquid fairly easily. A temperature of 28 degrees below zero, Fahrenheit, is enough. If ammonia is put under pressure, it can be turned into a liquid even at ordinary room temperature.

A gas that is so easily turned into a liquid is most useful. When a liquid evaporates, it absorbs heat from its surroundings. It has to, in order to give its molecules the extra energy they need in order to break loose from the liquid. (If you put a drop of water or, better, alcohol on your hand and blow gently on it, you will find that the skin beneath the evaporating liquid grows cool.)

If ammonia is put under pressure and made a liquid, and if the pressure is then relieved so that it evaporates quickly and becomes a gas again, it withdraws a lot of heat from its surroundings. If this is repeated over and over again, it keeps on withdrawing heat. Refrigerators and freezers are kept cold in this way. Ammonia is a *refrigerant*, It is not the safest refrigerant there is, for if the coils containing it spring a leak, the escaping gas could be very uncomfortable and even dangerous. It is about the cheapest, however, and is therefore often used in large industrial refrigerators.

Liquid ammonia has many chemical resemblances to water. Some people have even speculated that on planets colder than the earth, oceans of ammonia might exist as liquid. A whole system of chemistry (and even some form of life, perhaps) might exist based on ammonia, as on the earth it is based on water.

LAUGHING GAS

Nitrogen can be made to combine with oxygen (if we go to considerable trouble) in several different ways. The most familiar such combination is a gas, *nitrous oxide*. Its molecule contains two atoms of nitrogen and one of oxygen.

Nitrous oxide breaks up easily into nitrogen and oxygen. The mixture that results is one-third oxygen. This is richer in oxygen than the air about us—rich enough, in fact, so that a smoldering splinter thrust into a test tube of nitrous oxide will burst into flame. The heat of the smoldering tip breaks down the nitrous oxide, and the oxygen does the rest.

Nitrous oxide is an *anesthetic;* that is, inhaling it (mixed with oxygen) will cause a person to become insensitive to pain. It was so used for the first time in the 1840s when a dentist tried it on himself. It is still used today both by dentists and by surgeons. Small amounts of nitrous oxide sometimes have queer effects on people, making them behave hysterically. They may fight, cry, or laugh. It is for this reason that nitrous oxide is often called *laughing gas.* Actually it is no laughing matter. Nitrous oxide can kill people, too.

Anesthetics, in fact, are ticklish things in general. During surgical operations they are usually administered by specialists, who, through long experience and careful training, know exactly what they are doing.

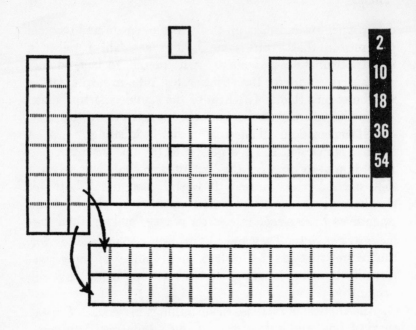

CHAPTER 4　**Helium**

THE SELF-SUFFICIENT ELEMENT

DISCOVERY IN SUNLIGHT

The white light of the sun is really a mixture of all possible colors. If the light is passed through a triangular piece of glass called a *prism*, it is spread out into a kind of rainbow. The rainbow is called a *spectrum*.

When elements are heated to a high temperature, the light they give off breaks up into bright lines of different colors when passed through the prism. Each element has its own set of lines. If you know the exact position of the lines in a spectrum, you can tell which element must be giving off the light. It was in this way that astronomers learned what elements are present in the sun and in other stars.

In 1868, during an eclipse of the sun, a French astronomer, Pierre Jansen, and a British astronomer, Sir Joseph Norman Lockyer, noted strange lines in the spectrum. They didn't belong to any known element. Lockyer decided that they must be caused by a new element, and he called it *helium,* from the Greek word for "sun."

In 1898 a British chemist, Sir William Ramsay, was studying a gas that came out of a certain kind of uranium ore. Among other things, he tested the kind of light it gave off when heated. He was amazed to find that its light, on being passed through a prism, broke up into exactly the same lines that Lockyer had noted in sunlight. Here we have an element that was found in the sun thirty years before it was discovered on the earth.

Helium is element No. 2. Next to hydrogen, it is the simplest atom known, and for that reason, probably, it is the second-commonest element in the universe. Of all the atoms in the universe, 90 percent, as we have seen, are hydrogen. More than 9 percent are helium. All the other atoms put together make up less than 1 percent.

Helium is *very* rare on the earth for the same reason for which hydrogen is *fairly* rare. Helium is so light and its atoms move so quickly that it cannot be held by the earth's gravity. The large outer planets have considerable helium in their atmospheres.

Helium is much rarer on the earth than hydrogen. For one thing, there was less to start with. For another, the helium atom is completely self-sufficient. It seems to have no tendency to combine with other atoms. Helium atoms don't even combine with one another; so helium gas is made up of single atoms moving around in complete isolation. It is *monatomic,* whereas gases like oxygen, hydrogen, and nitrogen with two atoms in their molecules are *diatomic* and ozone is *triatomic.*

Some hydrogen remained behind on the earth because it was tied up in the form of compounds with other, heavier atoms. Helium formed no compounds at all, so practically none of it was saved.

THE SAFE GAS

If you look at the periodic table on pages 16-17, you will see that element No. 2 (helium) is one of a group that includes the elements numbered 10, 18, 36, 54, and 86. All these elements resemble one another in certain ways. The most important resemblances are that they are all gases and that their atoms will not combine with other atoms of any kind. All are monatomic. For this reason, the whole group is referred to as the *inert gases.* Some people seem to think there is something aristocratic about this aloofness. For that reason the group is sometimes called the *noble gases.*

Their inertness makes these gases even more useful, in some ways, than nitrogen. Metals, as we have seen, are sometimes welded under a stream of nitrogen. But some metals are so active when heated that they will even combine with nitrogen. When such metals are welded, helium will take the place of nitrogen. Nothing will combine with helium.

Helium, because it is so light, is a good substitute for hydrogen in balloons and dirigibles. The helium atom is twice as heavy as the hydrogen molecule but is still only one-seventh as heavy as air. Helium has 93 percent of the lifting power of hydrogen, and that is good enough. Furthermore, it has two big advantages over hydrogen: first, since it will not burn under any circumstances, there is no danger of fire or explosion; second, since its atoms are heavier than the hydrogen molecule, helium doesn't leak through the gas bag as fast as hydrogen.

Where did we get the helium to use in dirigibles? There is helium in the air, to be sure, but less than one atom in every million. Picking out that one atom from all the oxygen and nitrogen and getting enough helium to fill the gas bags in a huge dirigible would be too expensive a job.

The helium came from gas wells and oil wells in the southwestern United States. These wells produce the mixture of inflammable gases called *natural gas*, which is sometimes piped to houses for use in cooking, and some of them produce helium, too. The helium may be only 1 or 2 percent of the total output, but separating it from the natural gas is quite easy. The United States was one country, therefore, that had enough helium to use in dirigibles and enough left over to sell to other countries. (The United States refused to sell any to Germany in the 1930s, for political reasons, and the *Hindenburg* had to use hydrogen.) However, even with helium, dirigibles were a failure because many of them, when caught in storms, buckled or broke.

Helium is the least soluble of all known gases. It is less than half as soluble as nitrogen. For this reason, deep-sea divers sometimes have a special air pumped down to them, an air that is 20 percent oxygen, like ordinary air, but 80 percent helium instead of nitrogen. Helium, and all the other inert gases, are suffocating but not poisonous. Helium, in fact, is less harmful than nitrogen, for it dissolves less in the blood and tissues, and the diver can therefore be lifted quickly to the surface with less danger of the bends.

A helium-oxygen mixture is lighter than a nitrogen-oxygen mixture and is easier to pump in and out of the lungs. It is therefore sometimes given to patients who have asthma or patients under anesthesia who are having difficulty in breathing.

Because of its lightness, helium is sometimes used in wind tunnels. The helium is expensive but it can be driven at high speeds more easily than ordinary air (much heavier than helium) can be. Planes can be tested for endurance against the quickly moving helium.

If you have ever bought one of the floating balloons sold at parades and county fairs, you have handled helium. That is what those balloons contain.

THE LOWEST ZERO OF ALL

There are several kinds of temperature scales. The most familiar one here in the United States is the *Fahrenheit scale*. On this scale, ice melts at 32 degrees and water boils at 212 degrees. Room temperature is about 75 degrees ordinarily, and body temperature is between 98 and 99 degrees.

In countries outside the United States, Great Britain, and certain parts of the British Commonwealth of Nations, the *centigrade scale* is used. On this scale ice melts at zero degrees and water boils at 100 degrees. (This is a much more convenient arrangement.) Room temperature is about 25 degrees, and body temperature is about 37 degrees. A centigrade degree is 1.8 times as large as a Fahrenheit degree. Scientists all over the world, even in the United States and Great Britain, use the centigrade scale only.

Molecules, you probably remember, are continually moving in a sort of vibration. The higher the temperature, the faster they vibrate. The lower the temperature, the slower they vibrate. Can there be a temperature so low that molecules come to a complete halt?

Yes. The temperature at which molecules stop moving is called *absolute zero*. It is the lowest possible temperature. Absolute zero is 273 degrees below the centigrade zero. That temperature is zero on the *absolute scale*. A degree on the absolute scale is of the same size as one on the centigrade scale. On the absolute scale, ice melts at 273 degrees and water boils at 373 degrees. Room temperature is 298 degrees, and body heat is 310 degrees.

Now the helium atom is so aloof that it won't even associate with others of its own kind to form a liquid unless the temperature is so low that the atom is hardly moving. Of all substances known, helium is the most difficult to liquefy.

On the absolute scale, for instance, with zero the lowest possible temperature, oxygen becomes a liquid at 90 degrees. Nitrogen must be cooled further; it becomes a liquid only at 78 degrees. Hydrogen is still worse; it becomes a liquid at 20 degrees. But helium won't become a liquid until the temperature has reached a depth of 4 degrees! Only at 1 degree does helium become a solid and then only when it is put under great pressure.

At the low temperatures of liquid helium, odd things begin to happen. Some substances, such as mercury and lead, lose all resistance to an electric current. They can carry an electric current forever. This is called *superconductivity*. Substances which are superconductive lose this property, however, if too much electricity is sent through.

Special switches made up of tiny hair-like wires are built in which tiny currents can be turned on and off at liquid helium temperatures as the wires gain and lose superconductivity. These are called *cryotrons*. Perhaps in the future, computing machines may make use of these tiny switches and then a machine which now takes up an entire large room may be made small enough to sit on a desk Of course, it would have to be dipped in liquid helium ir order to work.

Below a temperature of 2.2 degrees, helium itself gain; such unusual properties, it is given the special name o: *helium II*. Helium II conducts heat with greater rapidit) than any other known substance. It can make its wa) through holes so small that air couldn't pass through them It coats glass and flows upward along the sides of a beaker, over the lip, and down, a phenomenon which is called *superfluidity*. Chemists are particularly interested in these strange properties because they must work up new theories of matter to explain them. Liquid helium at temperatures above 2.2 degrees shows none of these odd properties and is called *helium I*.

THE FIRST INERT GAS

The first inert gas was discovered in 1894 by Lord Rayleigh and Sir William Ramsay (who, four years later, found helium on the earth).

This gas had given the first hint of its existence back in 1785, when a British scientist, Henry Cavendish, forced the nitrogen in a quantity of air to combine with oxygen by passing an electric spark through the mixture. He found that a tiny bit of the gas simply refused to combine, whatever he did.

One hundred years later, Rayleigh found that nitrogen from the air was just a little bit heavier than nitrogen prepared from chemicals. He decided that air must contain an unknown element that was heavier than nitrogen. He and Ramsay carefully fractionated liquid air and found the new element. It was No. 18. Because its atoms refused to combine with other atoms, they named it *argon* from a Greek word meaning "lazy."

Argon is the commonest of the inert gases. It makes up about 1 percent of the air. It is now used in light bulbs instead of nitrogen because it is even more inert than that gas and has even less effect on the white-hot metal wire. It is also used in welding instead of nitrogen, for the same reason.

THE LIGHTS OF BROADWAY

Three other inert gases were found in liquid air by Ramsay in the 1890's. Element No. 10 was named *neon* from a Greek word meaning "new," at the suggestion of Ramsay's 12-year-old son. Element No. 36 was named *krypton* from a Greek word meaning "hidden." Element No. 54 was named *xenon* from a Greek word meaning "stranger."

The more complicated the atom of the inert gas, the easier that gas is to liquefy. Neon boils at 27 degrees absolute, a little higher than hydrogen. Argon boils at 87 degrees, a little lower than oxygen. Krypton boils at 120 degrees and xenon at 166 degrees. (I am not discussing element No. 86 now; it is the most complicated inert gas of all, and will come up more comfortably toward the end of the book.)

Except for argon, the inert gases are all quite rare. One million cubic feet of air contains 9,340 cubic feet of argon, but only 18 cubic feet of neon, 5 ¼ cubic feet of helium, 1 cubic foot of krypton and a mere 12 cubic inches of xenon. We can get enough of these gases out of liquid air, however, to put them to one interesting use. When they are put into long tubes (which can be bent into interesting shapes or made to spell out words) and an electric current is forced through them, brilliant colors result. Neon glows a beautiful red-orange and gives its name to the *neon lights* that shine on Broadway and other city streets. Krypton in such a tube gives a green or lilac light, xenon a blue or green light. Other gases are sometimes used for additional color effects.

Xenon is a particularly heavy gas and its complicated atoms stop x-rays quite well. Chest x-rays of people who have just taken a deep breath of xenon may give useful information about the lungs. In light bulbs, xenon allows the filament to be raised to a higher temperature so that a brighter light is possible.

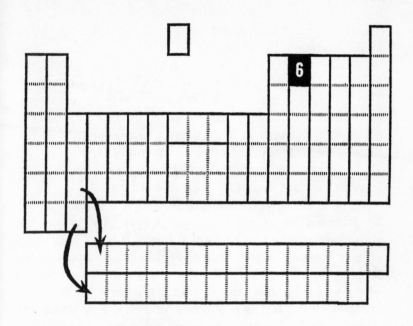

CHAPTER 5 **Carbon**

THE ELEMENT OF LIFE

THE ROCK THAT BURNS

The elements described so far in this book exist either as single atoms or as molecules made up of two atoms. Because their atoms or molecules have little attraction for one another, those elements are hard to liquefy. They remain gases at ordinary temperatures.

In *carbon*, however, element No. 6, each atom holds on

tightly to four other atoms, and each of the four clings
to four others. All the atoms in a mass of carbon hang
firmly together in this fashion. Instead of being difficult
to get them to stick together, it is difficult to pry them apart.
This means that carbon is a solid at ordinary temperatures.
It remains a solid even when heated red-hot. Eventually
it liquefies, but only at 3,500 degrees centigrade. It has the
highest melting point of all the elements.

You have seen carbon if you have seen *coal*. The name
"carbon," in fact, is from the Latin word for coal.

Coal is black, hard, and brittle, and it will burn. It has
been known for a long time, and people have often been
surprised to find a black rock that burns. It is not easy to set
aflame, however, and to keep a coal fire going requires some
skill. So, for a long time, men stuck to wood for fires; it was
easier to get hold of, and setting it afire was no problem.

Only in the last two hundred years has coal come into
general use for heating homes and for supplying energy to
run factories, make steel, generate electricity, and so on.

The importance of coal was at its height about 1900.
Since then, petroleum has been growing more important in
many ways, and atomic energy will play an increasing part
in the future. Even today, however, a strike of coal miners
is a serious thing; for lack of coal, steel mills, railroads, and
factories must quickly close down.

The atoms that compose coal were originally a part of
living things. All living creatures contain carbon. Fully 10
percent of the atoms in a human being are carbon.

Plants as well as animals are made up mainly (99 percent) of four kinds of atoms: carbon, hydrogen, oxygen, and
nitrogen. When plants that grow in marshy places die, they
slowly decay under the water into which they fall. The complicated carbon-hydrogen-oxygen-nitrogen molecules break

up into simpler molecules. These simpler molecules may be gases, like nitrogen or ammonia, or liquids, like water. These escape from the decaying plant material. In this way hydrogen, oxygen, and nitrogen atoms escape. Some carbon atoms also escape in the form of simple molecules, but most carbon atoms remain behind.

Decaying plant material thus comes to consist more and more of carbon. Dry *wood*, to begin with, is 50 percent carbon. In the first stages of decay, it becomes *peat*, which is 60 percent carbon. (In Eire, peat is still dug out of marshy places, dried, and used as fuel.) Slowly the peat is buried under accumulating mud and earth, and decay continues. *Lignite*, which is 67 percent carbon, is formed. (A hard, black variety of lignite, capable of taking a high polish, is called *jet* and is quite ornamental. It is not used much any more, but we still describe something which is very dark by saying it is as "black as jet.") More and more earth piles up. The pressure of the earth hastens the process. *Bituminous coal* is formed, and this is 88 percent carbon. Finally the process ends with *anthracite coal*, which is 95 percent carbon.

Now wood burns easily because, when it is heated, its molecules break down to simpler molecules that are given off as inflammable gases. These gases catch fire easily. The wood flame is yellow and smoky. As coal is formed underground, there is less and less of the gases to give off. Coal becomes hard to set aflame, but, once it does catch, a coal fire is much hotter than a wood fire. A pound of coal will deliver twice as much heat as will a pound of wood.

The flame of anthracite coal is practically without smoke. Bituminous coal still has enough atoms other than carbon to give a fairly smoky flame. If we all burned bituminous coal in our furnaces, the smoke would be inconvenient and even a danger to health. People therefore use anthracite in the home.

Bituminous coal is more abundant than anthracite. Factories and steel mills, which must use coal in quantity, use bituminous coal. It is for this reason that Pittsburgh, a great steel-making city, was notorious for its smoke. Particles of unburnt carbon in the air, as a result of coal fires, form a black *soot* which makes our cities dirtier, in some ways, than they were in the days of wood fires. Every year, about 400 to 500 tons of soot settle down upon each square mile of our larger cities.

It takes a lot of plant life to make coal. It has been calculated that a twenty-foot layer of decaying plant life is required to produce a one-foot layer of coal underground. When you think that there are trillions of tons of coal underground, you can imagine the numberless forests that must have grown, died, and decayed to give rise to all that, and the hundreds of millions of years it must have taken.

Carbon may be burned for reasons other than heat. If an electric current is set up between two carbon rods close together, a spark leaps across the gap. An intense white light results as the carbon slowly burns. Such an *arc light* can be used in motion picture projectors to form a light bright enough so that even when it is spread out over a large screen, it will give a brilliant picture.

HOME-MADE COAL

Before the use of coal became common, and when forests were more widespread in Europe and wood was cheaper than today, poor people made their own coal. They did this by taking quantities of wood, burying it in a pit, covering it with earth, and setting it on fire. If that wood had been set on fire in the open, it would simply have burned up, leaving only ash. Under the earth, though, there was a shortage of oxygen, and a good part of the carbon was left unburned. When the earth was finally removed, the black material left behind was almost pure carbon. Such carbon is called *charcoal.* Like coal, charcoal burns hotter, slower, and cleaner than ordinary wood.

This way of making charcoal was wasteful. Today, when charcoal is made by heating wood in the absence of air, the gases and liquids produced are saved and put to good use.

Very finely powdered charcoal has the ability to *adsorb* many types of molecules. This means that some kinds of molecules stick to the surface of the charcoal quite tightly. Usually, the larger the molecule, the better it sticks. Powdered charcoal is sometimes called *activated charcoal.*

Activated charcoal is used to decolorize substances. When sugar is being purified, for instance, it is only in the very last step that certain brown impurities are removed. (You can buy different grades of brown sugar in which some of the impurities are deliberately left behind to add flavor.)

The brown impurities have larger molecules than sugar has. When activated charcoal is added to the syrup that contains the sugar, the impurities stick to the surface of all the microscopic particles of charcoal, but the sugar itself does not. When the charcoal is removed and the syrup is evaporated, the sugar that is left behind is completely white. In this way, by adding a black powder to a brown syrup, we obtain a white substance in the end.

Activated charcoal is also used in gas masks. Air is sucked through a canister containing the charcoal before it reaches the nose and lungs. Oxygen and nitrogen molecules pass through easily. Poison gases with large molecules, however, remain behind, stuck to the small charcoal particles.

Powdered carbon is also called *carbon black* and its very blackness can be useful as in India ink, printing ink, and carbon paper. It is also added to rubber to strengthen it. That is why automobile tires, for instance, are black.

OPPOSITES, YET TWINS

The carbon atoms in coal and charcoal are arranged every which way, according to where they happen to be in the original wood. Solids in which the atoms exist higgledy-piggledy are called *amorphous* (from Greek words meaning "shapeless"). Solids in which atoms are arranged in orderly rows and columns are *crystalline*.

Graphite is a crystalline form of carbon. Deposits of graphite are found in the earth. Graphite can also be made from coal. If we heat coal by sending electric currents through it under the proper conditions, the carbon atoms slowly line up in regular order.

Graphite, like coal, is black and will burn if heated to 700 degrees centigrade. Below that temperature it is quite inert; it is used in stove polish, for instance, without fear of its burning.

The atoms in graphite occur in regular layers. These layers tend to split apart, so that graphite flakes easily. The small flakes slide over one another so readily that powdered graphite has a slippery feel and can in fact be used as a *lubricant*. If powdered graphite is put into a place where two solids are scraping and rubbing against each other, it will cut down the friction. It will coat the surfaces rubbing together, you see, and make them slippery.

Because flakes of graphite break off easily, graphite will make marks on paper if rubbed across it. (The word "graphite" comes from a Greek word meaning "to write.") The marks, of course, are flakes of graphite that are rubbed off and left behind as the graphite moves. The "lead" in your pencil is graphite mixed with clay. The clay makes the graphite harder and less likely to break.

Although the carbon atoms in graphite are regularly placed, they are not as close together as they can get. It sometimes happens that chunks of carbon far below the earth's surface are subjected to tremendous heat and pressure. Under those conditions, the carbon atoms are pushed as close together as possible.

When that happens, a second crystalline form of carbon results. This new crystalline form, although it is still pure carbon, just as graphite is, is as different in appearance as you can imagine. Whereas graphite is black and flaky, this new form is usually colorless and transparent. Graphite is rather soft and is used as a lubricant; this new form is one of the hardest substances known and, if powdered and placed among moving parts in machinery, would instantly ruin everything it touched. Graphite will conduct electricity, and rods of graphite are used in ordinary dry batteries (such as those in a flashlight) for that reason; the new form will not conduct electricity. Graphite is common and is used in pencils; the new form is rare and is used in jewelry.

The new form of crystal to which I am referring is *diamond*.

Yes, diamond is as much carbon as graphite or ordinary coal is. The only difference, really, is the way in which the carbon atoms are arranged. If a diamond is heated strongly, it will burn just as coal will. Naturally, few people care to try this experiment.

Diamond and graphite are allotropic forms of carbon, just as ozone is an allotropic form of oxygen.

In Chapter 4, I said that sunlight is broken up into a rainbow of color when it passes through a wedge of glass called a prism. This happens because glass refracts, or bends a light ray that hits it at an angle. It bends light of different colors by different amounts. The various colors in sunlight come out at different places at the other end of the prism, and the rainbow is formed.

All transparent substances do this more or less. Fine water droplets suspended in air do it. That is why we often see a rainbow when the sun first comes out after a rain.

The more a substance bends light, the more colorful the rainbow. Diamond bends light a great deal—much more than glass does, for example, or water. This means that a diamond, if cut properly, will give off different colors as it is turned in the light. Flashes of brilliant red, blue, green, and other colors emerge from the diamond, giving it a most beautiful appearance. Glass cut into the shape of diamonds lack these flashes. Such glass imitations are called *paste*. Sometimes paste is made more brilliant by adding strips of metal at the bottom; these are called *rhinestones*.

The world's supply of diamonds comes mostly from South Africa, where 96 percent of all diamonds are found. Even the richest diamond mines have only one ounce of diamond in 60 tons of rock. In 1955, laboratories at General Electric Co. have managed to duplicate the necessary conditions of temperature and pressure and have formed small "artificial diamonds." These artificial diamonds are exactly the same, chemically, as diamonds found in the earth. Calling them artificial is really unfair. They are the real thing.

Diamond is useful in industry. Since it is the hardest substance known, it can be used in drills and in tools designed to shape, cut, or polish very tough steels. It is an *abrasive;* that is, if powdered diamond is glued to a wheel, and that wheel is rotated rapidly, the super-hard particles of diamond will wear down any substance held against the wheel. Even other diamonds can be shaped and polished in this way. (This is, in fact, the only way in which diamonds can be shaped and polished.)

To be sure, the very best clear diamonds are not used in industry. They are too expensive. Anyway, only one diamond out of twenty is clear enough to be used as jewelry. Imperfect diamonds, in which the process of converting graphite to diamond has not been completed, and which are black because they still contain two to four percent graphite, are used in industry. They are called *carbonado* or *bort*. Although worthless as jewelry, they still have a diamond's hardness, and that is what industry needs.

MILLIONS OF COMPOUNDS

When wood is decomposing under water, some of the carbon does not remain behind. It escapes in the form of a compound with hydrogen. The molecules of this compound contain five atoms, one carbon and four hydrogens. Its chemical name is *methane,* and it is a gas at ordinary temperatures. Since it appears in the air over marshes (the water of which usually contains decaying wood), one common name for methane is *marsh gas.*

Some of the methane does not escape but is trapped in the coal as it is formed. If the coal is mined, methane escapes into the air of the mines as the miners break up the coal. This can be dangerous because methane, although not poisonous, is suffocating. It will also explode in air just as hydrogen will. Miners call the gas *fire damp*.

The carbon atom differs from all other atoms in the type of molecule it will form. Most atoms combine to form only small molecules, containing not more than a dozen atoms or so. Carbon atoms, however, also combine to form long chains or rings or combinations of the two. Carbon-containing molecules may consist of hundreds, thousands, even millions, of atoms. Only carbon can form molecules large enough and complicated enough to make life possible. No other element will do this. That is why carbon can truly be called the element of life.

Sometimes, when wood is decaying, both carbon and hydrogen remain behind. They do so in the form of numerous compounds consisting of chains and rings of carbon atoms to which hydrogen atoms are added. These carbon-hydrogen compounds are called *hydrocarbons*.

One naturally occurring substance that consists mostly of hydrocarbons is *petroleum*. The world's supply of petroleum may have originated from decaying wood, as coal did, but scientists are not certain of this. Petroleum, like coal, will burn. Being liquid, it will burn much more easily. The many types of hydrocarbons in petroleum can be separated from one another by fractional distillation (just as the oxygen and nitrogen in liquid air are separated). The hydrocarbons with small molecules boil at low temperatures; those with larger molecules boil at higher temperatures.

Some of the smaller molecules make up *gasoline,* which is burned in the engines of automobiles, motorboats, and airplanes. Still smaller molecules make up *petroleum ether,* which, under the name of *benzine,* is frequently used as a dry cleaner. Larger hydrocarbon molecules make up *kerosene, fuel oil, lubricating oil, petroleum jelly* (Vaseline), and so on. In the last half century, petroleum has become very important because of the development of the automobile and the airplane. Petroleum has taken over many (but not all) the jobs that coal used to do.

The simplest hydrocarbon of all is methane, which we already know, and that, too, is found in petroleum, as well as in marshes and coal mines. The natural gas that comes out of oil wells and is piped to houses for use in heating and cooking is 90 percent methane.

All hydrocarbons, plus similar compounds that contain oxygen, nitrogen, and other atoms in addition to carbon and hydrogen, are called *organic compounds*. They are called this because it was once thought that such compounds were produced only by organisms, or living things. In 1828, however, an organic compound was formed in the laboratory from mineral substances, and since then chemists have learned to manufacture hundreds of thousands of such compounds out of air, coal, and water.

There are more organic (carbon-containing) compounds known than all other compounds (without carbon atoms). Sugar is an organic compound. Starch, wood, olive oil, silk, cotton, nylon, celluloid, cellophane, paper, rubber, penicillin, and a million other things are organic compounds or mixtures of organic compounds. All living matter is made up of organic compounds. There is no end to them.

One of the main sources of organic compounds is petroleum. Another source is bituminous coal, which is only 88 percent carbon.

If bituminous coal is heated in the absence of air, the atoms other than carbon are given off in the form of compounds, and these compounds include some of the carbon. A ton of bituminous coal, heated in this way, will give off 10,000 cubic feet of *coal gas*. This consists mostly of hydrogen and methane. Coal gas, like natural gas, can be used in cooking and heating.

That same ton of coal will also yield ten gallons of black, pitch-like material called *coal tar*. (In ancient times, such

material was called *bitumen,* and that is where bituminous
coal gets its name.) Coal tar is a mixture of many organic
compounds, from which chemists manufacture beautiful
dyes, useful drugs, and innumerable other things. The nitrogen in the ton of coal separates in the form of twenty five
pounds of a compound called *ammonium sulfate.* This, too,
is most useful.

When all these substances have been driven off, what is
left behind is three-fourths of a ton of almost pure carbon.
This form of carbon, obtained from bituminous coal, is
called *coke.*

Coal can also be subjected to the reverse process. Instead of losing hydrogen atoms, hydrogen can be added.
In this way, coal can be converted into the more expensive
gasoline and other petroleum products. This is the same in
principle as the hydrogenation of fats which I mentioned in
Chapter 2.

THE AIR WE EXHALE

When carbon burns with a good supply of air, the carbon
atoms combine with oxygen to form a gas, *carbon dioxide.*
The molecule of carbon dioxide contains three atoms, one
carbon and two oxygens. This is true whatever form of carbon is burned, whether coal, coke, charcoal, graphite, or
diamond.

Even when the carbon forms part of a molecule containing other atoms, it still gives rise to carbon dioxide. Gasoline
(which contains carbon and hydrogen atoms in its molecules) forms both carbon dioxide and water when it burns.
In our bodies, as we saw in Chapter 1, organic compounds
(from the food we eat), containing carbon atoms in their
molecules, are slowly burned. One result of the burning is
that carbon dioxide is formed in our bodies.

Our breath is evidence of that. Fresh air contains a small quantity of carbon dioxide, one-thirtieth of 1 percent, to be exact; that is the air we inhale. The air we exhale is different; some of the oxygen has disappeared, and in its place is carbon dioxide. Carbon dioxide makes up about 4 percent of exhaled breath. (Carbon dioxide is also formed in volcanoes.)

You may wonder why the air doesn't gradually fill up with carbon dioxide and grow short of oxygen. Fortunately for us, plants use carbon dioxide to form organic compounds. In doing so, they liberate oxygen. Animals use up oxygen and produce carbon dioxide while plants use up carbon dioxide and produce oxygen, and thus a balance is maintained.

Carbon dioxide is suffocating and also somewhat poisonous. Air containing less than 5 per cent carbon dioxide can be breathed safely. Greater amounts of carbon dioxide will cause discomfort. Air containing 40 percent carbon dioxide would be fatal in a fairly short time.

When carbon dioxide is cooled to a temperature of 79 degrees below zero centigrade, it freezes into a white solid without first forming a liquid. If the white solid is allowed to stand at room temperature, it turns back into a gas without first forming a liquid. Liquid carbon dioxide will exist only at above-normal pressures. When a solid turns directly into a gas, without going through the liquid state, it is said to *sublime*.

Solid carbon dioxide is called *Dry Ice* (the name is a trademark) because it is used for refrigeration and doesn't turn liquid as ordinary ice does. We can see Dry Ice sublime if we put a small piece of it into water. The water churns and seems to boil furiously as the Dry Ice gives off carbon dioxide gas. (Dry ice is much colder than ordinary ice and must be handled with care.)

Carbon dioxide is fairly soluble in water. If it is put under pressure, it is even more soluble. Bottled soda pop contains carbon dioxide dissolved under pressure. When the pressure is relieved by our removing the bottle top, carbon dioxide comes out in tiny bubbles. Its presence gives the soda pop a pleasant tartness. The bubbles in beer and champagne are also carbon dioxide.

Carbon dioxide can be formed by the action of acids on certain chemicals known as *carbonates*. Fire extinguishers sometimes contain a carbonate solution and a bottle of strong acid. When an extinguisher is turned upside down, the acid pours onto the carbonate solution, and a stream of carbon dioxide gas and water comes out of the nozzle. Since carbon dioxide is one and a half times as heavy as air, it doesn't rise and float away but settles down on the burning material at which it is aimed; thus it keeps air away from the fire, and, since it won't support combustion itself, the fire goes out.

Baking powders contain a carbonate and a weak acid in solid form. The acid, as long as it is solid and dry, does not act on the carbonate. When such powder is mixed with the liquid ingredients of cake batter or biscuit dough, the acid dissolves in the liquid and then goes to work on the carbonate. Carbon dioxide is slowly formed. As the batter is heated, bubbles of gas fill it, and the cake rises. When baking is done, you can see that the cake is full of millions of small bubbles. It is these bubbles of carbon dioxide that make cake and baking-powder biscuits light and fluffy.

Yeast (which is a microscopic form of plant life) acts upon the starch in flour. In the course of its action it produces carbon dioxide. Yeast is generally used in the making of bread, and the carbon dioxide bubbles that result can be seen in any slice of ordinary bread.

GAS LEAKS AND AUTOMOBILE EXHAUSTS

When carbon burns in a limited supply of air, there isn't enough oxygen to supply each carbon atom with two oxygen atoms. Instead, each carbon atom is supplied with only a single oxygen atom. In this way, molecules of *carbon monoxide* are formed. Like carbon dioxide, carbon monoxide is a gas. The compounds differ in two important ways, however.

First, carbon monoxide is ready to accept that second oxygen atom for each molecule; in other words, it will combine with oxygen and burn. The molecules of carbon dioxide, on the other hand, have all the oxygen they can hold. Carbon dioxide is therefore non-inflammable and can even be used, as I have said, as a fire extinguisher.

Second, carbon monoxide is poisonous, much more poisonous than carbon dioxide. Air containing one-eighth of 1 percent carbon monoxide would be fatal for human beings in half an hour. If air contained as little as one-thousandth of 1 percent, that would still be enough to give a human being a headache.

Carbon monoxide is poisonous because it combines tightly with hemoglobin, the red coloring matter in the blood. It is hemoglobin's job to pick up oxygen in the lungs and carry it to all the tissues of the body. When there is carbon monoxide in the lungs, the hemoglobin picks that up instead and hangs on to it. It can no longer carry oxygen, and the body suffocates. Plants and bacteria are not affected by carbon monoxide, and neither are animals that do not have red blood.

Carbon monoxide is particularly dangerous because it is frequently met with in our industrial civilization. The burning gasoline in the automobile engine, for instance, doesn't get quite all the oxygen it needs; so some carbon monoxide is formed and sent out in the exhaust. In the open air that is not so bad; the carbon monoxide spreads out, and the individual molecules, as they strike oxygen molecules in the air, combine with the oxygen to form the fairly harmless carbon dioxide. If an engine is allowed to run in a closed garage, however, or if there is a leak from the exhaust pipe into the body of the car and the car windows are closed, the carbon monoxide accumulates faster than the oxygen in the air can take care of it, and death could be the result.

Another source of danger is the kitchen. Carbon monoxide, being inflammable, is often used in cooking gas. Coal gas, for instance, contains carbon monoxide and is poisonous for that reason. Then there is *water gas*. Water gas is formed when steam is passed over red-hot coke. The carbon atoms in the coke take the oxygen atoms out of the water, leaving the hydrogen atoms. The carbon atoms themselves are converted into carbon monoxide. A mixture of hydrogen and carbon monoxide is thus formed. Some methane is added, and the result is a good (but poisonous) cooking gas. Smelly compounds are often added to the gas to make sure that people smell a gas leak as soon as it starts and do something about it. (Do *not* look for the leak with a match. Open the windows instead, and call the gas company.)

If air is passed over red-hot coke, it will carry off carbon monoxide and the oxygen will be used up. The nitrogen will stay on, however. The mixture of nitrogen and carbon monoxide (which is called *producer gas*) is not a very good fuel, but it is a very cheap one and if used right on the spot can be very helpful.

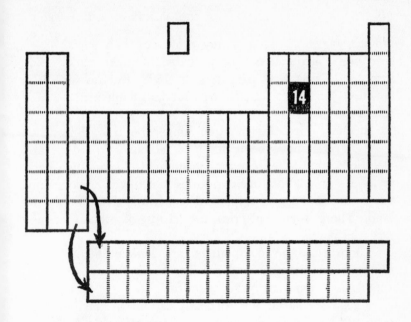

CHAPTER 6 **Silicon**

THE ELEMENT OF THE SOIL

TAKING CARBON'S PLACE

The second-commonest element in the rocks that make up the earth's crust is *silicon*, element No. 14. Out of every hundred atoms in the earth's crust, sixty are oxygen (which is the commonest element, of course) and twenty are silicon.

Silicon does not occur naturally in elementary form. For that reason, even though it is a common variety of

77

atom, few people, even among professional chemists, have seen pure silicon. It can be prepared in various allotropic forms, and was first prepared, in 1823, by the Swedish chemist, Jöns Jakob Berzelius, but as an element it has few uses.

In the future this may no longer be true. Recently, *solar batteries* have been designed which can produce an electric current when exposed to sunlight. So far, such batteries are only laboratory curiosities, but the day may come when they will be an important source of power for mankind. These solar batteries use strips of silicon as an essential part.

There are many compounds that contain silicon; most of them are common and familiar to us, many are very useful, and some are quite beautiful.

Silicon is placed just beneath carbon in the periodic table. It has many characteristics that resemble those of carbon. The atoms in a piece of crystalline silicon, for instance, are arranged in the same way as the carbon atoms in a piece of crystalline carbon. Silicon, like carbon, is therefore a hard solid. But, since silicon atoms are larger than carbon atoms, they cannot crowd as closely together as carbon atoms can and they can therefore be pried apart more easily. As a result, silicon is not quite as hard as carbon. Nor does silicon have as high a melting point. It melts at 1,420 degrees centigrade (carbon at 3,500).

Because of the similarities between the two elements, silicon atoms can sometimes take the place of carbon atoms. If coke (which is pure carbon) and sand (which contains silicon atoms) are heated strongly together by an electric current under the proper conditions, the silicon atoms from the sand replace half of the carbon atoms in the coke. We end with a substance made up half of carbon atoms and half of silicon atoms. This substance is called *silicon carbide* or, more commonly, *carborundum*.

Carborundum is harder than silicon but not as hard as diamond (which is pure carbon). Still, carborundum is harder than almost anything else besides diamond. What's more, it is much cheaper than diamond. Carborundum is frequently used in industry for grinding and polishing things that do not require the extreme hardness of diamond. Its melting point being 2,700 degrees centigrade (halfway between that of silicon and that of carbon), it is used as a furnace lining. Its advantage over carbon is that even at very high temperatures it will not burn.

Silicon will replace carbon under more glamorous conditions. Sometimes dead organisms, as they decay underground, do not turn to coal. Instead, if the conditions are right, the carbon atoms are slowly replaced by silicon atoms from the soil. As a result, with the passage of many years, a kind of stony replica of the organism is formed. The replica still shows the original shape and even much of the anatomical detail. What's more, it is now immune to decay and further change. It can last for hundreds of millions of years. Such stony remnants are called *fossils*. It is from a study of fossils that scientists have learned what they know about primitive life on the earth and how it changed and developed with time.

The process by which fossils are formed is called *petrifaction*. In the Painted Desert of Arizona, the remnants of many trees of ancient, ancient times are preserved in this fashion. The stony remains are called the Petrified Forest.

SILICON IN CHAINS

Silicon atoms can form chains the way carbon atoms do. Since silicon atoms grip one another much less tightly than carbon atoms do, their chains are weaker then those of carbon and break up easily. Only short chains can exist for any length of time. But silicon atoms and oxygen atoms, placed alternately, can form chains that are as long as carbon chains and are even more tightly held together. Groups made up of carbon and hydrogen atoms can be attached to the silicon atoms in such chains. The substances that result from all this are the *silicones*.

It is only in the last ten or twenty years that much has been done with silicones. There are many varieties, depending on the length of the chain and the kind of carbon-containing groups attached. Some silicones are used as lubricants and varnishes. They are particularly useful for such purposes because they are hardly affected by a degree of heat or cold that would quickly make ordinary oils and greases useless. They are also used to cover surfaces with a water-repellent film, and as hydraulic fluids, artificial rubbers and so on.

Perhaps you've seen one kind of silicone called Silly Putty or Bouncing Putty. The silicon-oxygen chain in Silly Putty is so long that the substance is a very stiff liquid. It is so stiff, in fact, that it seems to be a soft solid, much like putty or modeling clay. It resists any attempt to change its shape suddenly but yields if the attempt is made slowly. If you throw a piece of it against the floor or wall, it will be flattened quickly but will spring back stubbornly to its original shape and, in doing so, will bounce, just as a rubber ball will. On the other hand, if you squeeze it slowly, you can easily mold it in any way you wish. If you let a lump of it sit inside a jar, it will slowly settle down, like the liquid it really is, and fill the bottom of the jar snugly.

Silicones are water-repellent. Paper tissues treated with silicone are sometimes used to wipe the lenses of eyeglasses. This puts a thin, transparent layer of silicone over the glass. The layer clings tightly and keeps the lenses from steaming up easily when you step out of the cold into a warm room. For similar reasons, silicones are used in some kinds of car wax.

SOLIDS TO LOOK THROUGH

The silicon atoms that occur all about us are generally in a compound with oxygen. Molecules of this compound contain one atom of silicon and two of oxygen. The compound is called *silicon dioxide* or, sometimes, *silica*.

Notice that silicon behaves like carbon in this respect, too. (In the preceding chapter, I talked about carbon dioxide, molecules of which are made up of one atom of carbon and two of oxygen.) Here, however, is an important difference between carbon and silicon. Carbon dioxide is a gas. Silicon dioxide is a solid that is just as hard to melt as silicon itself.

Silicon dioxide, all by itself, makes up 12 percent of the weight of the rocks and soil in the earth beneath us. Silicon dioxide also combines with other substances to form *silicates*. The silicon dioxide that occurs in silicates makes up another 48 percent of the rocks and soil. No less than 60 percent of the earth's crust, therefore, is made up of silicon dioxide in one form or another.

Most of the common elements occur in organisms and are essential to life. Oxygen, hydrogen, nitrogen, and carbon are examples I have already discussed. Silicon, however, is an exception. Despite their being so common, silicon atoms are of no use in living tissue. The reason for this, probably, is that silicon dioxide and silicates are not soluble in water. There are practically no silicon compounds in the oceans, consequently, and it is in the oceans, not in the soil, that life developed.

The purest silicon dioxide found in nature is *quartz*, or *rock crystal*. Quartz is a clear, colorless, transparent, glass-like substance. It is even more transparent than glass, absorbing less of the light that passes through. Quartz is actually the most transparent known solid. (Ordinary glass is a silicate, and so the two substances are somewhat related.)

Quartz has certain advantages over glass. For one thing, it is not so affected by change of temperature. Most solids expand slightly when heated and contract when cooled. If hot water is poured into an ordinary glass container, the glass along the inside of the container expands as the hot water strikes it. The glass on the outside of the container remains cool until the heat travels through the thickness of the glass and heats it all up. Until that happens, a strain is set up in the structure of the glass. Part of it is expanding, and part of it isn't. What happens, often, is that the glass cracks, or even shatters, and the strain is relieved in that way. The same thing may happen when cold liquid is poured into a glass container that has just been washed in hot water.

In order to prevent such cracking, glass-makers make containers of thinner glass so that heat can reach all parts of the glass in less time. Or they use special kinds of glass that don't expand or contract much with changes in temperature.

Quartz is very good for such purposes. For a particular change in temperature, it expands or contracts only a sixteenth as much as glass. A vessel made of quartz could be heated red-hot and then plunged into cold water without cracking. A glass vessel so treated would splinter into a million pieces.

Another advantage quartz has over glass is that ultra-violet rays will pass through it. Ultraviolet rays will not pass through glass. For that reason the sun lamps with which people get indoor tans must use quartz and not glass in the light bulb.

Except for special uses, however, quartz is not likely to replace glass. The thing that saves glass is its cheapness. Quartzware is many times as expensive as glassware. This is not because quartz itself is expensive. It is because quartz is very hard to manipulate. Ordinary glass softens between 600 and 900 degrees centigrade (depending on the variety) and can then be easily blown and shaped. Quartz, however, does not soften till a temperature of 1,500 degrees centigrade is reached, and the utmost skill is required to handle it then.

VARIETY!

Silicon dioxide is usually found in impure forms; that is, small amounts of various other substances are mixed with it. Since the amounts and kinds of these substances differ, impure silicon dioxide can have a number of appearances.

A very common kind of impure silicon dioxide is *flint*, a kind of stone. The impurities present are enough to make the silicon dioxide lose its transparency. Flint is notable for its hardness and the fact that it forms a sharp edge when it breaks. Primitive man, for a long time, made his knives and weapons out of flint, and that era is therefore known as the Stone Age. In more recent times, but still in the days before matches, people struck steel against flint in order to get sparks. Bits of the steel were rubbed off against the hard flint and were heated to the glowing point by the friction. (This method of getting sparks is still used in cigarette lighters.) The words "silica" and "silicon" come from the Latin word for "flint."

Prettier varieties of impure silicon dioxide are *chalcedony*, which is semi-transparent or sometimes milky, and *agate*, which has striped markings. An agate composed of alternate bands of white and black is called an *onyx*. When the bands are white and red (or brown), it is a *sardonyx*. Agate, or a glass imitation of it, is sometimes shaped into spheres and used as playing marbles, which are then called "aggies." Still another variety of impure silicon dioxide is the purple or violet *amethyst* and the red to orange *carnelian*.

These substances are examples of *gems*. A gem is any glassy crystal that is hard, durable, and pleasing to the eye. Gems can be placed in metal settings, as in rings and necklaces, or they can be carved into various shapes, as in cameos. Depending on how rare and expensive they are, gems are divided into precious and semi-precious stones. The diamond is a precious stone, the agate a semi-precious stone.

Quartz and other forms of silicon dioxide are often broken up, by wind, rain, and temperature change, into small grains. These grains of silicon dioxide are *sand*. The purest forms of sand are quite white. The kind you find at the average beach, because of impurities, is usually of various shades of tan or brown. Sometimes sand is cemented together by natural processes to form *sandstone*.

Silicon dioxide can be prepared from silicates in the form of very porous fragments. Each piece is honeycombed with tiny air passages. This form of silicon dioxide is called *silica gel*.

Silica gel is useful because it will adsorb water vapor on the surfaces of its air passages. It is therefore a *desiccant*. Moist air forced through a container of it comes out dry. It often happens that electrical equipment won't work well if the air is too moist, and canisters of silica gel must be placed in strategic places within the equipment. This is particularly true in steamy, tropical climates. During World War II, some types of radios and radar equipment could scarcely have served their purpose in the South Pacific without the help of materials like silica gel. When a bit of silica gel has adsorbed all the water it can hold, we heat it to drive the water off. It is then ready for use all over again.

A natural substance somewhat similar to silica gel is formed of tiny skeletons made of silicon dioxide. The microscopic creatures called diatoms surround themselves with a protective layer of silicon dioxide. When they die, they decay, of course, but the skeletons remain behind, unchanged. Billions of them accumulate and form what is known as *diatomaceous earth*. This can be used to absorb undesirable impurities out of a liquid, much as charcoal can. It can also be used as an abrasive. It is also used to absorb nitroglycerine. The combination, called *dynamite*, is far less dangerous to handle than nitroglycerine alone.

Diatomaceous earth sometimes occurs as *opal*, which ranks as a gem. The more beautiful varieties of opal show flashes of different colors as the gem is moved. This characteristic is called *iridescence* or, from the name of the gem, *opalescence*. Opals that show this iridescence against a yellow or orange background are *fire opals*. Those that are iridescent against a black background are the rarest and most expensive.

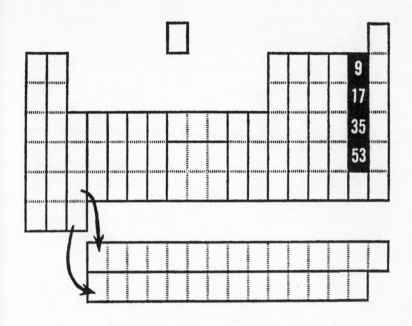

CHAPTER 7　**Chlorine**

THE GREEN ELEMENT

WAR BY CHEMICAL

On April 22, 1915, during World War I, the Germans trundled several metal cylinders up to the front lines and opened the valves. A greenish gas escaped and was blown over to the French lines by the wind. Two days later, they tried it again against a sector held by Canadian troops. In each case, the Allied troops found themselves surrounded by an irritating, choking, bad-smelling vapor that they could not withstand. They were forced to retreat.

Nobody is sure why the Germans didn't take advantage of the big openings that formed in the line opposing them, but they did not. Perhaps the success of the new method of attack caught them completely by surprise. Perhaps they suspected a trap. Whatever the reason, they lost their chance. By the time they tried again, the Allied troops had worked up simple forms of gas masks. In a few months, the Allies were using gas attacks of their own.

The poison gas first used by the Germans was *chlorine*.

Chlorine is element No. 17. It is a gas at ordinary temperatures, and its molecule is made up of two chlorine atoms.

It differs from the gaseous elements oxygen, hydrogen, and nitrogen in several important ways. In the first place, it is not colorless. It is a rather unpleasant greenish yellow; the name of the element, in fact, comes from the Greek word for "greenish yellow." This name was given the gas in 1810 by the British chemist, Sir Humphry Davy, who first recognized it as an element. It had been known for 36 years prior to that, but everyone before Davy had been sure it was an oxide and kept trying to break it down to oxygen and a substance they called "murium." They failed.

Chlorine is easier to liquefy than the other gaseous elements. It becomes an amber-yellow liquid at 34 degrees below zero centigrade. It is stored in cylinders in liquid form —under pressure, of course.

Chlorine is a fairly heavy gas, two and a half times as heavy as air. This is one characteristic that made it suitable as a war gas. Ammonia vapors also would be very unpleasant for soldiers, but ammonia is lighter than air; it would float away; the wind would scatter it easily.

Chlorine, being heavy, clings to the surface of the land and thins out more slowly.

As a poison gas, chlorine was soon replaced by still heavier and more poisonous gases. One of these was *phosgene*. The molecule of phosgene contains a carbon atom, an oxygen atom, and two chlorine atoms. It is a very dangerous gas indeed. It actually has a delightful fragrance (I once smelt a very small quantity of it; so I am a personal witness to that), but one good lungful is the end. Many of the other poison gases developed in those years contained chlorine atoms in their molecules.

Nevertheless, as we shall see, chlorine does far more good than harm.

MORE ACTIVE THAN OXYGEN

Chlorine is an active element; it is, in fact, more active than oxygen (though not as active as ozone) and will attack many substances more quickly.

It will support some kinds of combustion. A jet of burning hydrogen, for instance, will continue to burn if inserted into a jar of chlorine. At ordinary temperatures, mixtures of hydrogen and chlorine will do nothing at all if they are in the dark. If the mixture is exposed to light, however, it will explode. Apparently the light rays start the hydrogen and chlorine molecules to combining. Many chemical reactions are encouraged by light and by ultraviolet rays. These are called *photochemical reactions*.

Carbon, however, will not burn in chlorine. A burning candle, inserted into a container of chlorine, will start giving off a thick, black smoke. The molecules of wax in the candle contain carbon and hydrogen atoms, and only the hydrogen combines with the chlorine. The carbon atoms remain untouched and are liberated as finely divided soot.

The poisonous properties of chlorine are partly due to its activity. Chlorine attacks the membranes of the eyes, nose, throat, and lungs and damages them. Chlorine will also attack bacteria, however, and kill them; so even its poisionous nature can be turned to good use. Many cities purify their water supply by adding small amounts of chlorine to the water. Once cities adopted this policy of *chlorination*, diseases such as typhoid fever, which were spread by polluted water, became less common. The water in many swimming pools is kept disinfected by chlorination. So is sewage.

Chlorine is rather soluble in water. A pint of cold water will dissolve four pints of chlorine gas, and what results is *chlorine water*. The chlorine molecules combine with the water molecules to a certain extent (and with other molecules that may be present) to form *hypochlorites*. These hypochlorites are active substances that bleach colored substances the way ozone and hydrogen peroxide do. (If you want to know what chlorine smells like, smell a bottle of household bleach such as Clorox. The hypochlorites it contains are slowly breaking up, and a little bit of chlorine is always being formed. That chlorine is what you smell.)

Chlorine and hypochlorites are the most important bleaches in industry. They are easy to handle, and they are cheap. They are used in large quantities to bleach paper pulp and such plant textiles as cotton and linen.

SALT-FORMERS

When hydrogen burns in chlorine, molecules containing one hydrogen atom and one chlorine atom are formed.

The new substance is *hydrogen chloride*. It is a gas with an odor even more irritating than that of chlorine. Hydrogen chloride is very soluble in water. A quart of cold water will dissolve over 25,000 cubic inches of the gas.

When in solution, hydrogen chloride tastes intensely sour and behaves in certain ways that chemists consider typical of acids. A hydrogen chloride solution is therefore called *hydrochloric acid*. Hydrochloric acid is a strong acid. It is one of the three important strong acids, which, because of their strength and cheapness, are of major importance to industry. (A second acid is nitric acid, which I mentioned on page 46 The third, the most important of all, will be described in the next chapter.)

Hydrochloric acid is the best example of an acid that does not contain oxygen atoms in its molecule, despite what Lavoisier thought (see page 26). It does contain hydrogen, of course, as do all acids.

Hydrogen chloride is an example of a whole group of compounds formed by the combination of chlorine atoms with one other kind of atom. These are called the *chlorides*. The most common and most important chloride of all is ordinary *table salt*.

Chlorine in the form of chlorides is essential to the structure of living organisms. Blood, sweat, and tears are all salty. That is because they contain chlorides. It is because our body requires these chlorides that we put salt into our foods. Animals (particularly plant-eating animals that don't get a supply of salt out of the blood and tissues of other animals) will travel a long way and undergo many dangers to lap at places where there are natural accumulations of salt, the "salt licks."

It is in the form of salt that chlorine most frequently

occurs on the earth. The oceans are nearly 3 percent salt. There is enough salt in the oceans to cover the United States with a layer two miles thick.

Occasionally inland seas begin to evaporate faster than new water enters. When this happens, salt accumulates, since only the water evaporates. The Great Salt Lake in Utah and the Dead Sea on the border of Israel and Jordan are examples. When such tracts of water evaporate completely, vast deposits of salt are left behind, sometimes a thousand feet thick or more.

Salt, if it is melted, can be electrolyzed just as water can. Chlorine is one of the substances set free.

The elements related to chlorine (those in the same column of the periodic table) form compounds similar to salt. These elements are therefore referred to as the *halogens*, from Greek words meaning "giving rise to salt."

ORGANIC CHLORIDES

Although carbon and chlorine won't combine with each other directly, there are roundabout ways of bringing them together. Because of carbon's particular ability to make large molecules, thousands of chlorine-containing organic molecules are known. Two simple molecules of this type are the most familiar.

One is *chloroform,* the molecule of which contains one carbon atom, one hydrogen atom, and three chlorine atoms. Chloroform is a liquid that boils at a lower temperature than water. It evaporates more quickly than water at ordinary temperatures. Such easily evaporating liquids are said to be *volatile*. Chloroform is an anesthetic. It will put people to sleep, if properly used, and make them insensitive to pain. It was first used as an anesthetic in 1847, and one of the patients on whom it was first used was Queen Victoria of England. Chloroform has a bad effect on the heart, lungs, and kidneys, however, and has long since been replaced by safer anesthetics.

A closely related substance is *carbon tetrachloride*. Its molecule has no hydrogen atom at all, just one carbon atom and four chlorine atoms. Like chloroform, carbon tetrachloride is a volatile liquid. Since it is completely non-inflammable, it is used in some kinds of fire extinguishers. If it is pumped onto a fire, it quickly changes to a vapor. This vapor is much heavier than air, over five times as heavy. It clings closely to the fire and, since it will neither burn nor support combustion, puts it out.

Carbon tetrachloride will dissolve fats, oils, and greases very easily. For that reason, it is used as a dry cleaner. It is more expensive than petroleum ether, the other common dry cleaner. It is also more poisonous, and people using carbon tetrachloride in the home must remember to keep the room well ventilated. The great advantage of carbon tetrachloride is that it is the one dry cleaner that is not inflammable; its use does not present a fire hazard.

THE MOST ACTIVE ELEMENT OF ALL

The halogen with the smallest atom is *fluorine*, element No. 9. Like chlorine, fluorine is a pale, green-yellow gas, but it is much harder to liquefy than chlorine is. It liquefies at about the same temperature as oxygen. It is more poisonous than chlorine and even more active. It is, in fact, the most active element known. Its molecules (containing two fluorine atoms apiece) will attack and combine with almost anything; they will even react with water, dragging the hydrogen atoms away and leaving the oxygen atoms behind. Fluorine does this with such vigor and energy that some of the oxygen remaining is converted to ozone. Fluorine is even more active than ozone.

For this reason, liquid fluorine is being thought of in connection with rocket propulsion in place of liquid oxygen. The activity of liquid fluorine, however, makes it hard to handle.

When fluorine and hydrogen react, the molecules of each must split in two to form single atoms. The energy required to do this is great and is subtracted from the rocket thrust developed by burning hydrogen in fluorine. If, somehow, we could split the molecules to begin with and introduce *atomic hydrogen* and *atomic fluorine* into the fuel tanks, we would have the most powerful chemical fuel imaginable. However, we haven't the glimmer of a notion yet as to how to go about splitting such molecules and making them stay split.

If hydrogen is blown through an electric spark, for instance, the molecules break up into atomic hydrogen. However, those atoms recombine almost at once and liberate tremendous heat. Such an *atomic hydrogen blowtorch* produces temperatures of 3500° C.

Fluorine holds on to other atoms so tightly that chemists had a hard time separating it from its compounds. For a long time, when anyone did manage to yank it out of a compound, it attacked whatever it met up with and was immediately back in compound form again. Finally, in 1886, a French chemist, Henri Moissan, turned the trick. He electrolyzed a fluorine-containing compound with platinum equipment. (Platinum is one of the few substances that fluorine will not attack.) He kept the gas that resulted in a container he carved out of *fluorspar*. (Fluorspar is a mineral. Its molecule already holds all the fluorine it can;

so it is not attacked any further by the gas. In the same way, copper or other metals can be used for the purpose. The fluorine attacks the copper, but in so doing forms a hard tight layer of *copper fluoride* all over the metal. When the layer is complete, the fluorine has no further action.)

Fluorspar is a solid that melts fairly easily when heated. Since liquid fluorspar will combine with impurities in metal and remove them, it is used in the refining of metals. Such a material is called a *flux*. Because liquid fluorspar will flow, as any liquid will do, and because it was this flowing over impure metal that interested metal-workers, the mineral got the first part of its name from the Latin word for "flow." And, since fluorspar is the commonest fluorine-containing mineral in the world, chemists gave a similar name to the element.

Fluorine is not essential to life, but it does occur in the human body in small quantities, and it may turn out to be very important. Some years ago it was observed that the people who lived in Deaf Smith County, Texas, had practically no cavities in their teeth. Dentists were very much interested in this. They investigated the diet of those people. Eventually they discovered that the drinking water in that county was unusual in that it picked up small quantities of *fluoride* from the soil. (Fluorides are compounds of fluorine and one other element.)

Teeth also contain small quantities of fluoride. People began to wonder then if it was the fluoride in teeth that kept them from decaying. Perhaps adding fluoride to the diet would help.

Since fluorides are poisonous, chemists and dentists moved slowly and carefully. In the last few years, however, many towns have been adding tiny quantities of fluoride to their water—about one ounce of fluoride to every 8,000 gallons of water. This is not enough to do harm, and it is hoped that it will do a great deal of good.

Fluorine will combine with hydrogen to form *hydrogen fluoride,* a gas. The most interesting thing about this compound is that it is one of the very few that will attack silicon-containing compounds. When it does so, *silicon tetrafluoride* is formed. This is a gas, which escapes from the surface of the silicon-containing compound. The surface is thus eaten away, or *etched.*

Since glass contains silicon, hydrogen fluoride will attack it and leave a rough, cloudy surface in a very short time. This is put to good use. Glass is first covered with a thin layer of wax. Lines, numbers, or letters are then scratched in the wax, uncovering the glass at those places. If the waxed glass is then exposed to hydrogen fluoride, the wax is not affected, but the glass is roughened and etched wherever it shows through. After a short while the glass is removed from the hydrogen fluoride, and the wax is peeled away. And there, as permanent cloudy areas on the glass, are all the lines, numbers, and letters that had been drawn in the wax. If any glass utensils in your home have cloudy markings on them, this is the way the marks were made.

Fluorine, being a small atom, can take the place of the small hydrogen atom in hydrocarbon molecules. The fluorine atom holds on to the carbon atom even more tightly than hydrogen does. The resulting *fluorocarbons* are very inert substances. They are non-inflammable and are not affected by water, air, or strong chemicals (even by fluorine). Chemists have only begun to study these compounds, which will probably become important and useful in the near future. They are already being used as lubricants and solvents in special cases. One variety, called *Teflon,* put out by Dupont and made up of large molecules containing carbon and fluorine atoms only, is used as an electrical insulator.

A most interesting fluorine-containing compound is Freon. Its molecule contains one carbon atom, two chlorine atoms, and two fluorine atoms. It is a gas that liquefies at 28 degrees below zero. This is nearly the same temperature as that at which ammonia liquefies, and Freon can be used as a refrigerant just as ammonia can (see page 50). Freon has certain advantages over ammonia. Since it is odorless and not poisonous, the results of a leaking refrigerator would not be particularly dangerous or even unpleasant. Freon is used in household refrigerators and freezers for this reason. But, since it is considerably more expensive than ammonia, large industrial refrigerating systems still make use of ammonia.

THE LIQUID ELEMENT

The halogen next under chlorine in the periodic table is *bromine,* element No. 35. It is a dark-red liquid, one of the very few elements that are liquids at ordinary temperatures. It is volatile and boils at 59 degrees centigrade, evaporating as a rather beautiful red vapor. Even at room temperature, the air in a half-full bottle of bromine will appear reddish because of evaporation from the liquid. The beautiful vapor has such a strong and penetrating odor that the name of the element was formed from the Greek word for "stench." (To be truthful, however, it has always seemed to me that bromine doesn't smell nearly as bad as dozens of other chemicals.)

Bromine is not as active as fluorine or chlorine, but it is still active enough to do damage if breathed or if spilled on the skin. It must be handled very carefully. Sometimes chemists dissolve a bit of it in water (it is not quite as soluble as chlorine, but some of it will go in), and the resulting bright-red *bromine water* is safer to handle.

Bromine is considerably rarer than fluorine or chlorine. There is a hundred times as much fluorine in the world as bromine, and two hundred times as much chlorine. Bromine occurs in sea water in the form of *bromide* (a combination of bromine with one other element). It was first discovered in 1826, by a chemist, named Antoine Jérôme Balard, who was studying the solid contents of sea water after ordinary salt had been removed. There is much less bromide in the sea than chloride, only a five-hundredth as much, in fact.

Theoretically, any element could be obtained from sea water, since the sea contains at least a tiny bit of everything. And since there is so much sea water, even tiny bits would add up. The question is whether it would take so much time, trouble, and energy to collect the bits little by little out of all that water that the element would be too expensive. There are millions of tons of gold in the sea, but getting that gold out by any process we know today would be much more expensive than working away at ordinary gold mines.

Bromine is one element that can be profitably extracted from sea water. Two plants have already been established on the coast of the United States (one in North Carolina and one in Texas) to carry out the extraction. One pound of bromine is obtained from 1,800 gallons of ordinary sea water. If the water is from an inland sea that is drying up, such as the Dead Sea, even more bromine can be obtained. And bromine can also be obtained, of course, from the salt deposits left behind by dried-up seas. This means that we can never run out of bromine. All the bromine we extract and use eventually finds its way into the soil and is dissolved by rain and washed back into the sea by the rivers. The sea is, therefore, a permanent source.

Bromine is chiefly used to form an organic compound called *ethylene dibromide*. This compound is added to gasoline containing certain anti-knock compounds. The bromine combines with atoms in the anti-knock compound and prevents it from caking out in the automobile engine and doing harm.

Bromides are sometimes used in medicine as *sedatives;* that is, they quiet jumpy nerves and hysteria, making a person dull, quiet, and sleepy. If too much is taken over too long a period, bromides can be habit-forming and harmful. They should not be used except under a doctor's supervision. The term "bromide," by the way, has come to be applied to boring people or boring statements because they, too, can make a person dull, quiet, and sleepy.

MORE CHANGES IN THE DRINKING WATER

A still heavier halogen is *iodine*, element No. 53, a gray-black solid, which sublimes, when heated to 185 degrees centigrade, into a beautiful violet vapor. The name of the element, in fact, comes from the Greek word for "violet."

Iodine is the least active of the halogens mentioned, but it is still active enough to kill bacteria. In addition, it is the one halogen gentle enough to use directly on a wound. For this purpose, iodine is dissolved in a mixture of water and alcohol (it dissolves only very slightly in water alone). Such a solution is reddish-brown. A solution of a chemical in alcohol is called a *tincture* by pharmacists, and so it is *tincture of iodine* that we buy in a drugstore.

The strongest such tincture that is commonly used contains 7 percent iodine. (It also contains an *iodide,* which is a compound of iodine and one other element, to make the iodine dissolve more easily.)

As we all know, tincture of iodine is painted on minor cuts and abrasions to kill bacteria and reduce the danger of infection. It is an *antiseptic.* Once painted on, the iodine gradually sublimes away from the surface of the skin. If the wound is covered with a dressing, the subliming process is slowed up, and iodine may remain on the cut long enough to injure the tissues. It is better, therefore, not to dress a wound that has been painted with iodine, or to use gentler antiseptics if a dressing is necessary.

Iodoform, an iodine-containing compound, is also an antiseptic. Its molecule contains a carbon atom, a hydrogen atom, and three iodine atoms. (Do you notice the similarity to chloroform as described on page 92?) It is a yellow solid and is dusted on wounds and dressings. When people say that something "smells like a doctor's office," it is the smell of iodoform they mean. It is used less nowadays just because of that smell.

In very small quantities, iodine is necessary to human life. The human body contains about 1/600 ounce of iodine. One-third of that quantity is located in a small mass of tissue called the *thyroid gland,* which is near the Adam's apple. The thyroid gland controls the rate at which the body burns its foodstuffs to get energy. It does this by means of certain iodine-containing compounds called the *iodothyronines.* When iodine is scarce, the thyroid gland sometimes swells and forms in the neck an unsightly bulge called a *goiter.*

You may think that, since the body needs very little iodine, there would be little danger of scarcity. But iodine is not a common element. There are places where the soil contains very little of it. As a consequence, plants that grow in that soil have little iodine and so do the animals that feed on the plants or on one another. In such regions, goiter is (or was) fairly common.

Now that the cause of goiter is known, small quantities of iodides can be added to city reservoirs, and the supply is taken care of. Another way of taking care of man's need for iodine is to add small quantities of iodide to ordinary table salt. Many of us use this iodized salt. If you sniff at the opening of a container of such iodized salt, you will probably be able to smell iodine.

There is even less iodine than bromine in sea water—only about one ounce in two million gallons of sea water. It would be very difficult for men to collect the iodine out of all that water without making it tremendously expensive. Fortunately, some forms of sea life collect and store these iodine atoms for the needs of their own body chemistry. Seaweed and sponges are particularly good at this. Dried seaweed (called *kelp*) contains twelve pounds of iodine in every ton, which is much more than we would get from sea water. Iodine was first discovered in 1811 by a French chemist, Bernard Courtois, while he was studying the chemical composition of seaweed.

People who live near the sea are rarely troubled by goiter or iodine shortage. In the first place, they usually eat a certain amount of seafood, which contains enough iodine for the human body to get along on. Secondly, ocean spray drifting over the land near the sea usually deposits enough iodine in the soil to allow even land plants to have enough of it.

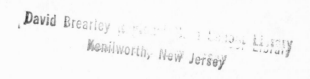

Iodine can also be obtained from the salt deposits remaining after seas have dried up; the nitrate deposits in Chile, which I mentioned on page 47, contain useful quantities of iodine. Iodine-containing water is sometimes found in the neighborhood of oil wells.

As a sort of frightful curiosity, there is *nitrogen tri-iodide*, with a molecule containing a nitrogen atom and three iodine atoms. It is a brown-black substance which is perhaps the most explosive substance there is. The gentlest touch of a feather will cause a crystal of nitrogen tri-iodide to let go with a loud bang. *Nitrogen trichloride,* with three chlorine atoms in place of the iodine atoms, is not quite so touchy, but has still caused terrible tragedies. Despite its explosive qualities, small quantities of nitrogen trichloride were at one time used to bleach flour.

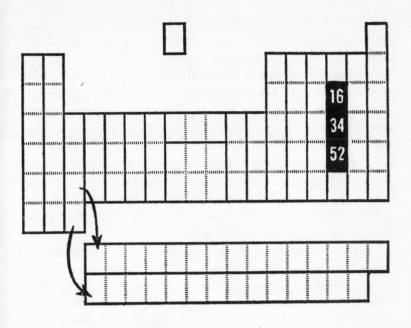

CHAPTER 8   **Sulfur**

THE YELLOW ELEMENT

FIRE AND BRIMSTONE

Element No. 16 should be familiar to all of us. It has been known to mankind since ancient times, but it was only in 1777 that it was recognized as an element. The man responsible for that is the same Lavoisier we have mentioned before in connection with oxygen, hydrogen, and nitrogen. The origin of the name "sulfur" is not known.

The ancient Greeks called it "theion," and for that reason sulfur-containing compounds sometimes contain the syllables "thio" in their chemical names.

Sulfur occurs just beneath oxygen in the periodic table, and sulfur atoms behave like oxygen atoms in many ways. If we just looked at the two elements, however, we would see no similarity at all. Oxygen is a colorless gas, and sulfur is a bright-yellow solid.

Sulfur exists in several allotropic forms. For instance, when molten sulfur is poured into cold water, brown strings of a rubbery substance are formed. This is called *plastic sulfur*. If this is allowed to stand, it slowly changes into the more familiar brittle yellow form.

Oxygen, sulfur and the other elements of this group are sometimes called the *chalcogens*. This comes from Greek words, meaning "to give rise to ores." The reason for this is that most *ores* (naturally occurring minerals from which metals such as aluminum, iron and copper can be obtained) are usually compounds of these metals with either oxygen or sulfur.

There are deposits of fairly pure sulfur underground in Sicily and in Louisiana and Texas. The best way to get the sulfur up to the surface is first to melt it. In this country a drill bores down until the underground layer of sulfur is reached. Boiling water is then forced down a pipe to the sulfur. Ordinarily, boiling water is at a temperature of 100 degrees centigrade, and this is not hot enough to melt sulfur. Sulfur melts at 113 degrees. But the boiling water forced down the pipe is under pressure. This pressure raises its temperature high enough to melt the sulfur. The molten sulfur is forced up through another pipe. This whole procedure is called the *Frasch process* after its inventor.

Sulfur is most commonly seen in one of two forms. If

liquid sulfur is boiled and the vapors are allowed to hit a cold surface, a fine yellow powder, known as *flowers of sulfur,* is formed. If liquid sulfur is simply allowed to freeze into solid chunks, you have what is frequently called *brimstone.* Sulfur is associated with the nether regions in another way. It only forms 0.03 percent of the earth's crust, but it grows more common in the deeper layers of the earth's structure. It is estimated that nearly 3 percent of the whole earth (not the crust alone) is sulfur.

The word "brimstone" may be familiar to you, and not in any pleasant way, either. That word brings up the fact that sulfur has a very unpleasant reputation. Some of this reputation is deserved, but not all of it.

When sulfur burns in air, with a sputtery blue flame, it combines with oxygen to form molecules of *sulfur dioxide.* Such molecules contain one atom of sulfur and two of oxygen. Sulfur dioxide is a gas with a very irritating, choking odor. Once people used to make candles out of sulfur and burn them in closed rooms as a disinfectant after sick people had been kept there. (We know much more about proper disinfection these days, and we don't burn sulfur candles any more.) Because of this, most people were familiar with the nasty "smell of sulfur." It was really the sulfur dioxide that smelled; sulfur itself has no odor at all.

Sulfur dioxide fumes sometimes rise out of cracks in the earth in volcanic regions. In Sicily, for instance, there are places where volcanic heat slowly burns sulfur underground to sulfur dioxide. People noticed this odor and noticed, too, that it came from underground. They recognized it as burning sulfur and remembered the eerie blue flame with which sulfur burns. Some of them decided that the underground fires of hell must be the result of burning sulfur.

For this reason, the "smell of sulfur" became associated with the devil, and preachers who threatened their congregation with the terrors of hell were sometimes said to be preaching "fire and brimstone."

CHEMICAL SMELLS

A great many sulfur-containing compounds besides sulfur dioxide have strong, unpleasant odors. The substances that give onions and garlic their odor and taste contain sulfur atoms. (This can be either good or bad, depending on whether we are eating them ourselves or smelling the breath of someone else who has eaten them.) The same is true of the substances that give mustard and horseradish their odor and taste.

A particularly foul-smelling group of sulfur-containing compounds are the *mercaptans*. You will get the idea right away when I tell you that a mercaptan accounts for the way skunks smell.

About the worst poison gas used in World War I was *mustard gas,* a garlicky-smelling compound that is a liquid, not a gas, at ordinary temperatures, but one that evaporates easily. The vapor is heavy and clings wherever the liquid has been sprayed. The gas is poisonous to breathe, and the liquid, if it touches the skin, causes blisters that are very slow to heal. Well, mustard gas is a sulfur-containing compound, too.

By now you are probably convinced that sulfur deserves everything bad that has ever been said about it. Yet sulfur atoms are found in many useful dyes, in sulfa drugs, in penicillin, and in at least two vitamins. Sulfur atoms, in fact, are necessary to life. All living tissue contains sulfur compounds.

The sulfur-containing compounds in our bodies, fortunately, have no odor. They can produce odors under certain conditions, however. Skin, hair, and feathers, for instance, have a lot of these compounds. If they are burned, they produce an unpleasant smell that most people describe as the "smell of burning feathers." Hair will do just as well. If you have a small tuft of hair to spare, set a match to it in an ashtray, and sniff the result.

Eggs also are rich in sulfur-containing compounds. When an egg has spoiled, these compounds break up into simpler molecules. Some of the molecules consist of two hydrogen atoms and a sulfur atom. This is *hydrogen sulfide*, a gas with a very unpleasant odor. Most people call it the "smell of rotten eggs."

Hydrogen sulfide, despite its smell, is a very useful chemical. It can be dissolved in water for easier handling, and then it will combine with any of a great number of different kinds of atoms to form *sulfides*. These sulfides behave differently. Some dissolve in plain water, some don't. Some dissolve in weak acids, some don't. Some dissolve in strong acids, some don't. If an unknown chemical is treated with hydrogen sulfide and the behavior of the sulfides that result is studied, it is often possible to tell what kinds of atoms were present in the unknown. This is an example of *chemical analysis*.

Many high-school and college chemistry courses are intended to teach chemical analysis, and the laboratories often smell strongly of hydrogen sulfide. When people talk about how a chemical laboratory smells, they are usually referring to hydrogen sulfide.

Hydrogen sulfide is quite poisonous, even more so than carbon monoxide. It is not as dangerous as carbon monoxide, however, because of its odor. By the time there's enough of it in the air to do considerable harm, the odor is unendurable. People open the windows or leave altogether. Hydrogen sulfide, in fact, is sometimes deliberately added to cooking gas. When this is done, a gas leak can be smelled at once, and there is less chance that the odorless carbon monoxide will sneak up on you. Mercaptans are sometimes added and then the odor from a leak is even more noticeable.

THE USEFUL SIDE OF BRIMSTONE

One of the amazing things about chemistry is that almost any substance, no matter how unpleasant it seems to be, can be put to good use. Rubber, for instance, wouldn't be much good without sulfur.

Rubber was first smeared on clothing to make it waterproof by a Scotsman named Charles Macintosh. (A raincoat is still sometimes called a mackintosh.) It kept the water out, but such clothing wasn't very convenient to wear. In cold weather the rubber was very stiff; in warm weather it was very sticky.

In 1839 an American named Charles Goodyear accidentally spilled a mixture of rubber and sulfur on a hot stove. When he scraped off the mess, he found that the rubber had more stretch and snap than before and that it stayed dry and flexible through a considerable range of temperature. He had discovered the process of *vulcanization*.

Sulfur is also mixed with carbon and saltpeter to form *gunpowder*. Sometimes one wonders whether this is a "good" use, but it is certainly an important use.

Sulfur dioxide, that cough-provoking, irritating gas, is a useful bleach. It can be used to bleach substances that would be damaged by chlorine's harsher action. Sulfur dioxide is used to bleach silks, woolens, straw hats, and feathers. Sulfur dioxide is easily liquefied and, like ammonia, it can be used as a refrigerant.

It is also used in tremendous quantities in the paper industry. Paper is made out of mashed-up wood. The most useful portion of the wood is a substance called *cellulose*. This occurs in fibers that are held together by a sticky substance called *lignin*. Sulfur dioxide in water solution forms what are called *sulfites*, and these sulfites, when added to mashed-up wood, dissolve away the lignin. The fibers of cellulose are left behind, and these can be pressed together, under the proper conditions, into thin, flat sheets of paper.

The molecule of sulfur dioxide can add another atom of oxygen. We then have *sulfur trioxide*. Sulfur trioxide can dissolve in water, and then the molecule of sulfur trioxide adds a molecule of water to form a molecule of *sulfuric acid*. The sulfuric acid molecule contains seven atoms altogether, two hydrogens, one sulfur, and four oxygens.

Sulfuric acid is a strong acid, the cheapest and most important of all. It has been said that you can tell how industrially advanced a nation is by the amount of sulfuric acid it uses up each year.

Sulfuric acid molecules combine with water molecules very eagerly and develop considerable heat in doing so. This can be dangerous since it is often necessary in chemical laboratories to *dilute* sulfuric acid—that is, to mix it with water and make it less strong. If this mixing is done too quickly, the heat that is formed will cause the mixture to boil and spatter. Chemists can be badly burned or even blinded in this way. The handling of sulfuric acid calls for the greatest caution.

Sulfuric acid, in its efforts to combine with water (which is made up of hydrogen and oxygen, as you may remember), will even take hydrogen and oxygen atoms out of other molecules. The carbon in organic molecules will be left behind. For this reason, sugar will turn black and fluffy almost at once if it is placed in sulfuric acid. Wood will slowly turn black. A drop of sulfuric acid will quickly eat a hole right through a piece of paper or through your clothes. It will cause a bad burn if it happens to touch bare skin.

It is one of the most useful chemicals known, and our modern industrial civilization could scarcely continue without it. We use it in refining metals and petroleum, in plating metals, in making steel wire, in making many different chemicals, and in a thousand other ways.

AUTOMATIC DOORS

Two elements, much like sulfur, occur below sulfur in the periodic table. The heavier one of the two, element No. 52, was studied by a German chemist named Martin Heinrich Klaproth in 1798. He named it *tellurium* after the Roman god of the earth. It had been discovered in 1782 by an Austrian chemist, Franz Joseph Müller.

Then, when Berzelius, whom I mentioned previously in connection with silicon, discovered element No. 34, in 1817, he realized that it was similar to tellurium; so he named it *selenium* after the Greek goddess of the moon. Earth and moon! This shows that even chemists sometimes have a streak of poetry in them.

Selenium and tellurium form compounds similar to those of sulfur. A selenium atom, for instance, will combine with two hydrogen atoms to form *hydrogen ·selenide*. This is even worse than hydrogen sulfide, for it smells like rotten radish. And then there's *hydrogen telluride,* which smells worse still, like rotten garlic. Chemists who have occasion to work with tellurium may pick up enough of the substance to get a tiny bit of hydrogen telluride in their breath. As you can imagine, this makes them social outcasts while it lasts. And yet small quantities of tellurium, added to certain other elements, result in some desirable properties, so that some chemists must continue to work with the stuff.

In some places in the western United States, there is more than the usual amount of selenium in the soil. Plants growing in such soil absorb the selenium. Then, when they make substances that should contain sulfur, they often get selenium atoms in the places where sulfur atoms ought to go. Such plants, loaded with selenium, are poisonous, and cattle grazing on them may be killed. A common name given to such plants is "locoweed."

Yet selenium, which is even more unpleasant than sulfur, also has its uses. If a bit of selenium is added to molten glass, it gives it a pinkish tinge that neutralizes the natural greenish color of glass. The result is to make glass clearer and more transparent. If more selenium is added, the glass turns a clear, deep red, and it can then be used in stoplights.

Selenium conducts electricity in a remarkable manner. In the dark it conducts electricity poorly; in the light it conducts electricity well. This was discovered in 1873 by Willoughby Smith. This is another one of those important discoveries which were made by accident, like the vulcanization of rubber. This behavior of selenium makes possible automatic doors and other marvels.

A *photoelectric cell* contains metal that is coated with

selenium. Such a cell may be attached to a post in front of a swinging door. From an opposite post a small lamp casts a beam into the photoelectric cell. The selenium being in the light, electricity flows, and the swinging door is held shut. When a person passes between the posts, his body breaks the beam of light. The photoelectric cell is in darkness for a short while. During that period of darkness, no electricity flows through the selenium, and, with the current broken, the door swings open just in time for the person to pass through it. Photoelectric cells can turn on alarms, turn off equipment, and do thousands of tasks in just this way.

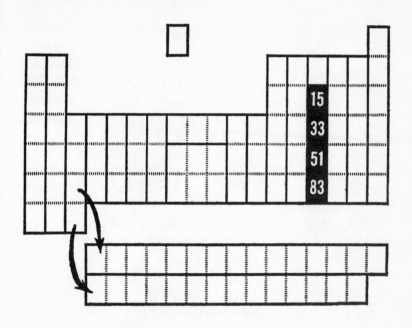

CHAPTER 9

Phosphorus

THE ELEMENT THAT GLOWS

MATCHES OF VARIOUS KINDS

Back in 1669, a German chemist named Hennig Brand was working with urine. He heated it till all the water was driven off. When he studied the solid matter left behind, he discovered a new element, No. 15.

This element was a soft, white, waxy substance that slowly burned at ordinary temperatures when exposed to air. It did so with a greenish glow. Because of this glow,

Brand called the new element *phosphorus* from Greek words meaning "I bear light."

Such phosphorus was used in the first matches because it could easily be made to catch fire. Unfortunately, phosphorus in this form (which is called *white phosphorus*) is very poisonous. People working in match factories could not help breathing a little of the phosphorus vapor. The phosphorus would then settle in their bones and damage them incurably. Swallowing 1/300 of an ounce of white phosphorus would be fatal. The use of white phosphorus had to be forbidden.

Fortunately, there are other allotropic forms of phosphorus. If white phosphorus is heated for a few hours at 250 degrees in the absence of oxygen (so that it won't burn), it changes into *red phosphorus*. This was discovered in 1845. The two forms of phosphorus are different not only in color but in other qualities. White phosphorus melts at 44 degrees, but red phosphorus doesn't melt until almost 600 degrees is reached. Red phosphorus is much less active than white phosphorus: it doesn't glow; it doesn't burn so easily. It is much less poisonous than white phosphorus, and it is quite safe to handle.

Modern matches still depend on phosphorus in one way or another. Ordinary matches that will light when struck on any rough surface contain *phosphorus trisulfide* in their heads. The molecule of this compound contains four phosphorus atoms and three sulfur atoms.

Phosphorus trisulfide is not particularly poisonous and is easy to set on fire. The heat produced by the friction of rubbing the match on a rough surface is enough to cause it to burst into flame and set fire to the wooden part of the match. In order to make sure this happens, special compounds that liberate oxygen when heated are also added. With oxygen present, the phosphorus trisulfide burns vigorously, as you can see for yourself when you strike a match.

Safety matches do not contain any phosphorus compounds in their head, and ordinary friction will not set them on fire. The special strip on the match box or match folder does contain red phosphorus. If a safety match is rubbed on this strip, the red phosphorus sparks, and the heat of the spark is enough to set the match on fire.

When phosphorus burns, *phosphorus pentoxide* is formed. This is a white solid, and its molecule is made up of two phosphorus atoms and five oxygen atoms. Phosphorus pentoxide, like silica gel (see page 85), is a desiccant. It will absorb water vapor out of the air and leave the air quite dry. It is a more powerful desiccant than silica gel, is one of the most powerful known, in fact, but it is hard to handle. If it is not taken care of at all times, it will absorb enough water from its surroundings to become gummy and useless before you know it.

When phosphorus pentoxide combines with water, it forms *phosphoric acid*. This is a medium-strong acid and it is produced in greater quantity than any other acid except sulfuric acid. Phosphoric acid combines with various types of atoms to form *phosphates*.

FLESH AND BONE

The fact that phosphorus was first found in urine should give you the idea that it occurs in living matter. So it does. Phosphorus is another of those elements that are essential to life. In the body, it always occurs in the form of phosphates.

The bones of human beings and of other bony animals, from elephants to fish, are composed mostly of a kind of phosphate. This bone phosphate is very similar in structure to a common kind of rock called *hydroxyapatite*. It may be startling to think that bones and stones are so alike, but they are. It is, of course, only the hard part of bones, the "mineral" part, that I am referring to here. Bones also contain complicated organic molecules, and stones do not. It is the organic molecules that make bones tough and flexible and enable them to stand a blow that would shatter them if they were made of phosphate and nothing more. As people grow older, the organic portion decreases in quantity, and the phosphate increases. That is why old people have brittle bones and are more likely to break them than young people are.

There is considerable phosphate in the soft tissues of the body, too. When the body burns foodstuffs to get energy, it stores this energy in the form of very special phosphates called *high-energy phosphates*. These high-energy phosphates break down very easily, giving up the energy that has been stored in them. Whenever the body requires some energy (to contract a muscle, say, or to send an impulse along a nerve, or to build up a complicated molecule out of simple ones), it breaks up some of these high-energy phosphates.

Since plants, like all other living things, need phosphates, too, many fertilizers contain phosphates. One of the most important and useful fertilizers, in fact, has the common name *superphosphate*. Ground bones can be used as fertilizer, too, because of the phosphate they contain.

Plants decaying under water produce methane, as you may remember (see page 69). Some of the phosphorus in their tissues is also given off in the form of *phosphine*. This is a foul-smelling and poisonous gas with molecules made up of one phosphorus atom and three hydrogen atoms. Phosphine will burn in air at ordinary temperatures. This dim flame of burning phosphine is sometimes seen in the air over marshes and is probably responsible for what has been called the *will-o'-the-wisp*. People lost in marshy country, seeing it, may think it is a person with a lantern or a light in a house window, and may proceed in that direction hopefully, only to be disappointed. For that reason, people who chase after something that can't be reached are sometimes said to be "pursuing a will-o'-the-wisp."

Phosphates are also found in animal wastes. On islands off the coast of Peru, there are vast deposits of wastes, called *guano*, produced by the hordes of birds that have dwelt there for ages. The guano is valuable as fertilizer for this reason.

A new group of phosphorus-containing compounds have made newspaper headlines recently. These are the so-called *nerve gases*. These compounds interfere with certain body chemicals that make it possible for nerves to work. If nerve gases are breathed, all the body's nerves are put out of commission. The body's functioning comes to a standstill since no muscle will work without nerve "messages." Death results in a few minutes. (You can imagine what would happen to a modern city if all its electrical wiring were suddenly put out of commission.) Nerve gases are deadlier than any of the poison gases used in World War I, and I hope that there will never be occasion to use them.

THE FAVORITE POISON

Immediately underneath phosphorus in the periodic table is element No. 33, *arsenic*. It was first recognized as an element in 1733, but in one form or another it had been known since ancient times. Its name comes from the Greek name of a yellow mineral that is a compound of arsenic and sulfur. Although not a common element, arsenic is very widespread. In preparing almost any metal from its ore, one of the problems is to get rid of the small quantities of arsenic that are obtained with the metal.

Mention arsenic to the average person, and he thinks instantly "poison." It is undoubtedly the favorite poison of detective-story writers. The funny thing is that the "arsenic" used to poison people both in real life and (much more often) in detective stories is not the element arsenic at all. Arsenic itself is not particularly poisonous. Instead, an arsenic compound, *arsenic trioxide,* is what is used. The molecules of arsenic trioxide are made up of two arsenic atoms and three oxygen atoms. As little as 1/200 ounce of this substance is fatal.

It is possible to get accustomed to arsenic if very small quantities are taken over a period of time. Such an "arsenic-eater" can end by taking several times the dose that would kill an ordinary person and not be harmed. An ancient king, Mithridates of Pontus, was supposed to have tried to make himself immune to all the poisons he knew by eating small amounts of them every once in a while. Probably this wouldn't work for all poisons, but it does for arsenic.

To see if arsenic is present in a dead man, a portion of his tissue is treated with a mixture of an acid and a metal. The acid and metal react with each other and give off hydrogen gas. At the same time, the acid and the hydrogen cause the arsenic in the tissue (if any is present) to change into *arsine.* This is an extremely poisonous gas with a molecule made up of one arsenic atom and three hydrogen atoms.

The mixture of hydrogen and arsine is led along a tube that is heated at a certain point. At the heated portion the arsine breaks up into arsenic and hydrogen. The arsenic settles out on the cool glass of the tube a few inches farther along as a gray patch. Such a patch proves the presence of arsenic. This is called the Marsh test after the man who developed it, and you can see how important it would be in some murder trials.

Arsenic trioxide, in combination with water molecules and some other kinds of atoms, forms *arsenates*, which are poisonous. You mustn't think, of course, that poison can be used only on human beings. Arsenates are important as insect-killers, or, to use a fancier name, as *insecticides*. We often spray fruit trees with arsenates to keep the fruit for us instead of for insects. (And it is a good idea for us to wash fruit before eating it since the arsenates are definitely not good for our health.) Arsenates are also spread over cotton fields, often from low-flying planes, in order to take care of the boll-weevil. The most familiar arsenate is *Paris green.*

Arsenic is present in some war gases. *Lewisite*, which, next to mustard gas, was the most unpleasant poison used in World War I, is an arsenic-containing compound.

Arsenic isn't all bad, however. Some of its compounds can be used as medicines. A German scientist named Paul Ehrlich discovered an arsenic compound, called *arsphenamine* or "606" (because it was the 606th compound he tried), that could be used, with caution, to cure syphilis. Nowadays, though, arsphenamine has been put out of business. Antibiotics do the job more quickly and more safely.

THE IMPORTANCE OF PROPER FREEZING AND MELTING

Arsenic's two heavier relatives are *antimony*, No. 51, and *bismuth*, No. 83. Both have been known since early times. Their names are old and of uncertain origin.

Antimony is a silvery-white substance that can be prepared in a number of allotropic forms. The most peculiar form is an unstable one called *explosive antimony*. The name means exactly what it says. If explosive antimony is scratched, it changes into more ordinary forms of antimony with explosive force and gives off a good deal of heat.

Explosive antimony occurs only in the laboratory. Natural forms of the element are never explosive.

Antimony doesn't have the evil reputation of its relative, arsenic, but in some ways it is no improvement. It forms a compound called *stibine,* with a molecule composed of an antimony atom and three hydrogen atoms. This is just like arsine with an antimony atom substituted for the arsenic atom, and stibine is just about as fearsomely poisonous as is arsine.

The ancient Egyptians used *antimony trisulfide* (with molecules made up of two antimony atoms and three sulfur atoms) as an eyebrow pencil. That was five thousand years ago. Nowadays we have a less romantic use for that substance. It is put in the heads of safety matches. Antimony trisulfide will burn, just as the similar phosphorus trisulifide will, but not as easily. The heat of ordinary friction isn't enough to make it catch fire. The spark of burning red phosphorus on the striking strip of the match box will do the job, however.

Antimony is one of the metallic elements (the others will be mentioned later) that are mixed together to form *type metal.* Type metal is an *alloy* (that is, a mixture of metals) with a low melting point. If it is melted, poured into a mold, and cooled, it will freeze, of course, in the shape of the mold. If the mold has the shape of a letter of the alphabet, the type metal will take that shape, and the result will be a piece of printing type. If a number of such molds are lined up in a row and the type metal poured into them is allowed to freeze in one piece, the result is a slug of type. If the face of this slug is covered with ink and pressed against paper, a line of printing appears.

You may think that any low-melting metal would do for the purpose, but that is not so. Most liquids shrink when they freeze. A liquid shrinking as it froze would pull away from the edges of the mold, and the final shape would not be clear-cut. Type metal is one of the few exceptions to this. It does not shrink as it freezes; it expands. Think of the liquid type metal expanding as it freezes, forcing its way into all the nooks and wrinkles of the mold. Perfectly shaped letters, clear and sharp, are formed.

Bismuth can also be mixed with other elements to form low-melting substances. Here it is the low melting point that is important. Some mixtures melt at temperatures even less than that of boiling water, and these are called *fusible alloys*. (The word "fusible" means "easily melted.") *Wood's metal*, which melts at 71 degrees centigrade, is a fusible alloy.

Wood's metal can be used in practical jokes. Spoons made of it can be served with hot tea. Then, while the victim is engaged in stirring his tea, he is kept talking and doesn't notice that the spoon bowl is melting as he stirs, until he finds himself moving a spoon handle around and around in air with nothing attached to it.

There are more important uses for fusible alloys. They are used in automatic sprinkling systems. Many factories and business places have sprinklers overhead that are all set to go. The only thing that keeps them from going is plugs of fusible alloy. Once a fire starts, the heat quickly melts those plugs. The sprinklers start working with all their might, and the fire, we hope, is then put out.

A more homely use of bismuth is in the form of *bismuth subgallate* (a compound with a rather complicated molecule.) This is used in antiseptic dusting powders for wounds. Other bismuth compounds of this sort are used to soothe upset stomachs.

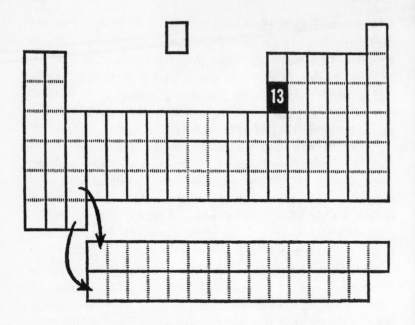

CHAPTER 10　**Aluminum**

THE ELEMENT OF THE KITCHEN

METALS AND NON-METALS

Elements can be divided into two groups. Most of them (eighty, to be exact) are *metals*. The remaining twenty-two are *non-metals*. I have used the word "metal" previously in this book, since I felt sure that you would know what I meant. You have all seen metals and have an idea of what a metal looks like.

Metals have a peculiar shine or gloss when they are polished. This is referred to as *metallic luster*. Non-metallic substances, whether elements or compounds, almost always are transparent or white or have flat colors without luster. Think of sulfur, for instance.

Metals are *conductors* of heat and electricity; that is, heat and electricity move easily through them. Electric wires are always made of metal. Radiators in cars and in houses are made of metal. Non-metals are just the opposite. They are *insulators* of heat and electricity.

Metals are *malleable;* that is, they can be beaten into thin sheets. They are also *ductile;* they can be drawn into threads or wires. You can't imagine non-metals like sulfur or carbon being beaten into sheets or drawn into wires. One blow would simply reduce them to powder. Metals are *flexible;* that is, they can be bent or twisted without breaking. If a thin sheet of sulfur were prepared by freezing molten sulfur on a flat surface, it would shatter at once if you tried to bend it.

Chemists try to distinguish between metallic elements and non-metallic elements by the names they give them. As often as possible, the names of metallic elements end with "ium." As often as possible, the names of non-metallic elements end with "n" or "ne."

Consider the twenty-one elements I have already discussed in this book. Nineteen of them are non-metals, and their names are hydrogen, oxygen, nitrogen, helium, neon, argon, krypton, xenon, carbon, silicon, chlorine, fluorine, bromine, iodine, sulfur, selenium, tellurium, phosphorus, and arsenic.

Thirteen of these elements have names that end in "n" or "ne." Of the remaining six, phosphorus, sulfur, and arsenic have old names that were given before modern notions of the elements were worked out. Helium was named when nothing was known about it except its spectral lines (see page 53), and Lockyer, who named it, thought it was probably a metal. (It should be called "helion," but it's too late now.) Finally, selenium and tellurium are borderline cases. Some allotropic forms of each substance are a bit metallic in behavior.

The two metals I have so far discussed are antimony and bismuth. Here again the names are old ones, given before modern notions of the elements were worked out.

All the non-metallic elements are crowded into one portion of the periodic table, by the way, as you can see in the accompanying diagram.

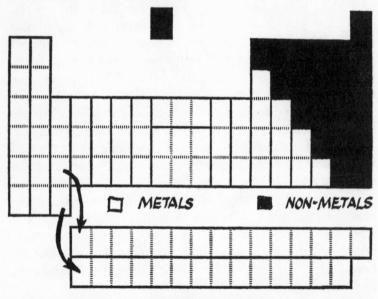

Of the eighty-one elements I have yet to describe and discuss only three are non-metals. (These three will not come up till the end of the book.) All the rest are metallic, and I shall begin by discussing the commonest metal of all.

That commonest metal is element No. 13, the name of which is *aluminum*. That name ends in "um," not "ium," but the British are more careful and remember the proper ending. They call the metal *aluminium*.

THE PRECIOUS METAL ALL ABOUT US

Aluminum is the third-commonest element in the earth's crust. Oxygen and silicon are the only commoner elements, and both of those are non-metals. Over 7 per cent of the earth's crust is aluminum. Aluminum occurs in the soil mostly in the form of various types of *aluminum silicates*. These are compounds of aluminum, silicon, and oxygen with one or two other common elements. Certain aluminum silicates containing any of a variety of other metals form the reddish gems called *garnets*.

The commonest type of rock on the land surface of the earth is *granite*. The continents, in fact, are really just huge slabs of granite set in another kind of rock called *basalt*. Basalt lies under the granite continents and also under the oceans.

Both basalt and granite are *igneous rocks;* that is, they were formed under the influence of the great heat far beneath earth's surface. Deeply buried rock, hot enough to be molten, is called *magma*, and when it pours out of volcanoes, it is *lava*. Molten rock which cools so rapidly as to form a hard, glassy mass is called *obsidian*. Lava may emerge from volcanoes filled with gas bubbles. It will then solidify into spongy light rock that will float on water. Such light rock is called *pumice*.

Granite is made up of three substances: quartz, feldspar, and mica. Quartz, as I explained in Chapter 6, is silicon dioxide. *Feldspar* and *mica* are both forms of aluminum silicates. Geologists sometimes refer to the continents as being part of the *sial* layer of the earth's crust. "Sial" is, of course, an abbreviation for silicon and aluminum.

One interesting type of feldspar is a dark-blue mineral called *lapis lazuli*, which is quite rare and can be classified as semi-precious. Artificial lapis lazuli is called *ultramarine*.

Mica can be split apart into thin transparent sheets, which are sometimes called *isinglass*. Sheets of mica can be used instead of glass when you want a certain amount of bending ability—for instance, in the rear windows of convertibles. It can also be used for windows in furnaces because mica will stand much more heat than glass will. Little fragments of mica compose the "snow" we use as part of Christmas tree ornamentation. Such snow is white and glistening and, most important, non-inflammable.

When quartz is broken into little pieces by the action of wind and weather, we have sand, as I explained in Chapter 6. In the same way, feldspar is weathered into *clay*. Particles of clay are finer than particles of sand and form a spongy mass that holds the rain and prevents it from evaporating too quickly. For this reason, clay is essential to soil fertility, even though living organisms have no use for either aluminum or silicon. (Neither element occurs in living tissue.) Clay mixed with sand and iron compounds is called *loam*.

Clay is one of the common and useful raw materials for building. *Bricks* are impure clay that has been baked to nearly 1,000 degrees centigrade. In addition to clay, bricks contain sand, and red bricks contain iron compounds. It is the iron compounds that give them the red color. Bricks are hard, durable, and fireproof.

A purer kind of clay, known as *kaolin*, is used in the

manufacture of *pottery* and *porcelain*. Porcelain is shiny (even partly transparent) and non-porous. When kaolin is fired so that it is not shiny, it is called *stoneware*. Kaolin fired at a low temperature, so that it remains porous is *earthenware*. All of us have eaten out of dishes made of fired kaolin, and a general name for such products is *ceramics*. Here we have our first examples of the uses that make me call aluminum the element of the kitchen.

Clay that has been put under pressure beneath the ground and has therefore been squeezed into a hardened mass is *slate*. Slate splits easily into flat slabs, and you have all seen it as blackboards in the classroom.

With sulfur, oxygen, and other elements aluminum forms a series of compounds called *alums*. Alums were known and named in early times, and it is from the word "alum" that the name "aluminum" is derived. The alums are *astringents;* that is, they pucker skin and other membranes of the body. When "styptic pencils," which contain alum, are touched to small cuts, such as those a man might get while shaving, the alum draws the skin together and stops the bleeding. Alums are also used sometimes to purify drinking water. They cause the bacteria in the water to clump together. The whole undesirable mess, bacteria plus alum plus other foreign particles, settles to the bottom, leaving the water above clear and free of germs.

Alum, or *aluminum sulfate* (a simpler version of the alum molecule) is used in "sizing" paper. It is added to wood pulp, along with certain gummy materials, and the two manage to cement the fibers together to form a continuous sheet. Aluminum sulfate is also added to textiles. It reacts with water to form very fine particles of *aluminum hydroxide*, which cling to the textile fibers tightly. Dye compounds, in turn, cling to the aluminum hydroxide more tightly than they would to the fibers themselves. Thus, aluminum sulfate is an example of a *mordant,* a compound which makes it easier to dye fabrics.

You would certainly think that, aluminum compounds being so common, aluminum metal would also be common and cheap. After all, next to sand, what could possibly be so dirt-cheap as clay?

That isn't the way it worked out at first. The aluminum atoms in these very common silicates hold on so tightly to the other atoms in the compound that it is almost impossible to pry them loose. A Danish chemist, Hans Christian Oersted, first isolated aluminum in 1825, but it wasn't until 1850 that aluminum was prepared for commercial use. Even then it was so difficult to get that a pretty high price had to be charged for it. It cost $90 a pound or more, which made it much more expensive than silver and almost as expensive as gold.

Napoleon III of France, who ruled in the 1850s and 1860s, used an aluminum fork (gold and silver were good enough for his guests), and his baby received the precious gift of an aluminum rattle. A large block of aluminum was displayed at the Paris World's Fair of 1855. It was called "silver from clay." By the 1880s methods of separating aluminum had slowly improved, and the price was down to about $5 a pound. When the Washington Monument was constructed in 1884, a solid aluminum cap was put upon it, and the cap is still there. It forms the pointed top that you can see in any picture of the monument.

ELECTRICITY DOES THE TRICK

Then, in 1886, something happened that changed everything. A young American chemist named Charles Martin

Hall, aged 22 and just out of school, discovered a way to prepare aluminum cheaply from *aluminum oxide* and was rich for the rest of his life. A French chemist, P. L. T. Héroult, discovered the same process about the same time. He was born in the same year as Hall (1863) and he died in the same year, too (1914).

Pure aluminum oxide is a white crystalline substance, whose molecules contain two atoms of aluminum and three of oxygen. A common name for it is *alumina*. A fairly pure form of naturally occurring aluminum oxide is *corundum*, and a less pure form is *emery*. These are both hard substances. They are not as hard as carborundum or diamond, but they are cheaper than either and are very useful as abrasives. Little pieces of synthetic corundum may be used as bearings in watches and other instruments. Corundum is very high-melting (it is *refractory*, in other words). It can therefore be used as a furnace lining. Brick can also be used, and is always used for home chimneys, for instance.

Many jewels (some very precious) consist of corundum, with small amounts of impurities that produce the color. Among these jewels are the yellow *topaz*, the blue *sapphire*, and the red *ruby*. Artificial rubies and sapphires can be made by adding the proper impurities to corundum. The gems may then be called "artificial," but they have exactly the same chemical composition as the natural stones. *Turquoise* is a trifle more complicated; it is a kind of aluminum phosphate.

The most useful form of aluminum oxide is *bauxite*, which occurs in considerable quantity in various parts of the world. It is first purified to get rid of silicon and other undesirable types of atoms and is thus converted to white powdered alumina. This alumina is dissolved in a molten mineral called *cryolite*, the molecule of which contains aluminum atoms and fluorine atoms as well as others. This is the key point of the discoveries of Hall and Héroult, this finding of a mineral in which alumina will dissolve on strong heating. As it happens, cryolite is found almost exclusively in western Greenland, so even that frozen waste contributed importantly to our modern civilization. Nowadays, synthetic cryolite, formed in chemical laboratories, is used.

The hot solution is kept in a carbon-lined vessel. Bars of carbon are inserted, and electricity is run through the solution between the bars and the lining. (Carbon, though not a metal, conducts electricity.) The aluminum oxide molecules are pulled apart by the electricity, and the aluminum atoms settle to the bottom of the vessel as the molten metal. (To this day, one of the major uses of electricity in industry is in the preparation of aluminum.)

Within a very short time after this new procedure was discovered, the price of aluminum dropped to thirty cents a pound and less. Aluminum became a cheap, plentiful metal, and a number of highly important uses were found for it.

THE IMPORTANCE OF BEING LIGHT

Men have been using metals in weapons and in construction for only about 6,000 years (and in most parts of the world for a much shorter time). Before that, for hundreds of thousands of years, men used stone.

Metal has several advantages over stone. Certain metals are considerably stronger than stone. A pillar of such a metal will support much more weight than a stone pillar of the same size. The metal is tougher and more flexible. A sudden blow might bend or distort the metal, but the same blow would shatter stone into pieces.

Metals also have certain disadvantages, compared with stone. One of them is weight. Many metals are heavier than stone and therefore harder to manipulate. If the great stone blocks that make up the Pyramids had been made of iron or steel, perhaps all the manpower of Egypt could not have put them into place. Even machinery would have been hard put to do it.

A substance that would combine the strength of metal with the lightness of stone would be very valuable. Aluminum comes close to being such a substance.

Aluminum is just about as heavy as granite or marble and is only one-third as heavy as iron or steel. A cubic inch of iron weighs about four and a half ounces. A cubic inch of aluminum (or stone) weighs only one and a half ounces. Aluminum is stronger than stone but not as strong as iron. An iron beam will support more weight than an aluminum beam of the same size.

We can strengthen aluminum by adding small quantities of other metals to it—making an alloy of it, in other words. Alloys usually have some properties that the separate metals don't have. There are hundreds of different alloys, each with its own characteristics and each with its own uses.

For instance, if to ninety-five pounds of aluminum we add four pounds of copper and half a pound each of two metals known as magnesium and manganese, we get an alloy called *Dural*. Dural is considerably stronger than pure aluminum. It is still not as strong as iron and its alloys, but it is strong enough for many purposes.

There are times when lightness is so important that we are willing to give up a little strength. In airplanes, for instance, lightness is the thing. Airplanes are made largely of aluminum. Aluminum is used in trains, trucks, and automobiles wherever lightness is more important than strength.

The lightness of aluminum is useful in another way. Aluminum is an excellent conductor of electricity. Some metals are better, but they are usually heavier and more expensive. A copper wire, for instance, will conduct electricity more easily than an aluminum wire of the same size, but the copper wire is over three times as heavy as the aluminum wire. If a thicker aluminum wire were used, one as heavy as the thin copper wire, the aluminum would carry electricity better. And the aluminum would be considerably cheaper, too. For this reason, though the electrical wiring in your home is made of copper, the transmission lines that carry electricity over long distances are usually made of aluminum.

A glamorous use of aluminum involves its efficient reflection of light. Thin layers of it are evaporated on telescope mirrors. It is the aluminum layer, in fact, that makes them mirrors.

THE IMPORTANCE OF PROPER CORROSION

Aluminum has another advantage over iron. Aluminum doesn't seem to rust or corrode. There is a peculiar reason for this. Aluminum is a more active element than iron, and it reacts with oxygen more quickly and easily. The very fact that aluminum corrodes easily is what keeps it from corroding more.

In combining with oxygen, aluminum forms aluminum oxide, which clings to the surface of the aluminum metal very tightly. As soon as a thin layer of aluminum oxide is formed (a layer so thin that it is completely transparent), the aluminum is completely protected from further corrosion. The aluminum oxide on the surface of the metal is inert and won't combine any further with oxygen. The aluminum metal itself is protected from oxygen by the aluminum oxide layer. To all appearances, then, the aluminum remains shiny and unaffected by air or weather. The aluminum oxide layer is made more permanent if the aluminum is dipped into a solution through which an electric current is passed. Aluminum treated in this manner is called *anodized aluminum*.

For this reason, aluminum is being used more and more to form outer walls, doors, window frames, rainspouts, and so on. It requires no painting or any particular care. If it is made of one piece, it won't warp, as wood might. Aluminum objects will bend or give way, of course, more easily than iron objects will; so there are many places where aluminum isn't likely ever to replace iron.

Most metals, when powdered, are black, no matter what the original appearance of the metal may have been, but aluminum powder is an exception. It is just as silvery and shiny in powder form as when it is all one piece. Aluminum powder can be mixed with linseed oil and made into *aluminum paint*. This can be painted onto surfaces from which you want to reflect light or radiate heat, or which you simply want to protect from corrosion. Aluminum is such an excellent light-reflector, when polished, that it is used on telescope mirrors, where it is important to have as much reflection as possible.

Aluminum is a good metal to make household utensils out of, and these days we all use aluminum pots and pans that Napoleon III would never have been able to afford. The aluminum conducts heat so well that food heats up quickly over a fire. It doesn't corrode and isn't affected by acids or other chemical substances in the food because the aluminum oxide layer protects it. (That layer protects the food, too, so that aluminum does not mix with or "poison" the food in any way, despite occasional housewifely nervousness on the subject. Neither iron nor aluminum is particularly poisonous in small quantities, anyway.) Aluminum is light, too, which is a blessing for a woman who has to sling the pots and pans about all day. You see, then, why aluminum can be called the element of the kitchen.

There is still another way in which we probably handle aluminum every day: in the thin, flexible sheets known as *foil*. Aluminum foil is used to wrap chewing gum, cigarette packs, margarine, and hundreds of other things that we buy in the stores all the time. Recently, too, housewives have begun to use aluminum foil in the cooking and storing of foods, making it more than ever the element of the kitchen.

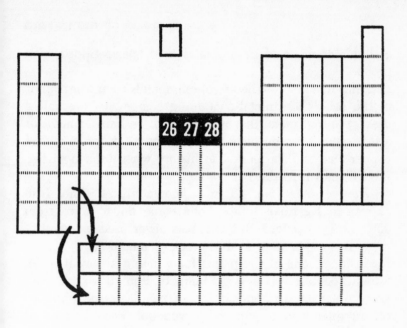

CHAPTER 11 **Iron**

THE STRONG ELEMENT

THE SECRET WEAPON

One of the oldest classics in literature is the *Iliad*, an epic poem that was supposedly written by a Greek named Homer about 800 B.C. It deals with a ten-year siege of a town called Troy by a Greek army. The siege took place about 1100 B.C. If you read the poem, you will find that the warriors wore armor made of bronze, carried swords

135

and shields made of bronze, and used spears tipped with bronze.

After mankind learned to obtain metals from compounds in the soil (these metal-containing compounds are called *ores*), the first metal that was found to be hard enough for armor and weapons was bronze. Bronze is an alloy of copper and tin. The period in history when bronze was so used is known as the *Bronze Age*.

Iron, element No. 26, was known at the time. Iron objects in Egyptian tombs have come down to us from 3500 B.C. and before. But iron was never used in quantity then. It was, in fact, a semi-precious metal. In the *Iliad*, for instance, one of the prizes for winning an event in an athletic contest was a large lump of iron. It wasn't until about 1500 B.C. that any group of people learned how to obtain quantities of iron from iron ore, enough of it to make weapons and armor with.

The first people who learned this were the Hittites, who lived in Asia Minor (modern Turkey) at this time. When they went out to fight with this new metal, their surprised enemies found themselves the victims of a "secret weapon." Bronze swords and spears were useless against an iron shield. The swords and spears bent and blunted. On the other hand, iron swords and iron-tipped spears cut through bronze shields and armor easily. Iron, you see, was considerably harder than bronze.

As knowledge of the new metal spread, group after group abandoned bronze for iron. Mankind entered the *Iron Age*. By 600 B.C., the conquering Assyrian armies used iron almost exclusively.

Iron is now the cheapest metal we have. Some forms of iron cost as little as a cent a pound. It is the second-commonest metal in the earth's crust, making up almost

5 percent of it. It is not quite as common as aluminum, but it is easier to get out of its compounds, and that cuts down the cost.

Iron grows commoner as one considers layers deeper and deeper underground. The earth's core, or center, some five thousand miles thick, is probably composed largely of liquid iron. If the composition of the whole earth is taken into account and not just the earth's crust, there is a greater weight of iron in our planet than of any other element. About 40 percent of the weight of the planet may be iron.

Earth collects iron from outer space, too. Uncounted swarms of solid particles (some as large as mountains, others as small as grains of dust) are circling the sun. Millions of these hit the earth's atmosphere every day. Almost all of them are burnt to vapor by friction with the air. Some of the larger ones get through the air and hit the earth's surface; these are called *meteorites*. About 90 percent of the meteorites we have found are composed largely of iron. (The rest, the "stony" meteorites, are composed of silicates.) The lump of iron offered as a prize in the *Iliad* may have been a meteorite.

Iron is one of the essential elements in living tissue. In human beings (and in other animals with red blood), iron forms a necessary part of the blood. The compound *hemoglobin*, which gives blood its redness, picks up oxygen from the lungs and carries it to all the tissues. Each hemoglobin molecule contains four iron atoms, and it is these iron atoms that carry the oxygen. A human body contains about a tenth of an ounce of iron altogether.

A human being who is short of iron suffers from a condition known as *anemia*. One way of treating anemia caused by shortage of iron is to feed the patient pills containing certain simple iron compounds.

IMPURITIES OUT AND IMPURITIES IN

The most important iron ore is an orange-red mineral called *hematite*, which is an iron oxide. Its molecules contain two iron atoms and three oxygen atoms. (Hematite is responsible for colorful rock formations in many parts of the earth and probably also for the ruddy color of the planet Mars.) A variety of this ore called *red ochre* has long been used as an artist's pigment. In very finely powdered form, it is called *jeweller's rouge*. It is used to polish glass into exact shape; particularly, telescope lenses and mirrors. Another iron ore is the blackish *magnetite*, which is another kind of iron oxide, with three iron atoms and four oxygen atoms in its molecule. These ores always contain silicates as impurities.

In order to get the iron metal out of these ores, men had to find some way to get rid of the silicates and also to free the iron from the oxygen atoms in the iron oxide molecules. They found they could do this by mixing the iron ore with coke and limestone (I shall talk about limestone in Chapter 13), putting the mixture into a *blast furnace*, sending a blast of hot air through it, and setting the coke (which is almost pure carbon; see page 72) on fire.

The oxygen in the air is not enough to take care of all the coke, however. As the mixture in the blast furnace grows red-hot, some of the carbon atoms of the coke combine with the oxygen atoms in the iron oxide molecules, setting the iron atoms free. This iron, now in the form of the metal, melts and settles down to the bottom of the furnace.

Meanwhile the limestone combines with the silicates to form *slag*, which also melts and settles down to float on top of the molten iron. Every once in a while, the molten iron and slag are drained off, and more iron ore, coke, and limestone are added at the top of the furnace. The furnace isn't shut off till the firebrick lining (made of high-melting aluminum oxide or aluminum silicate) is in need of repairs.

The iron obtained from such blast furnaces is called *cast iron* because it is poured into molds and freezes there. (Freezing a molten metal in a mold is called "casting.") It is also frequently called *pig iron*.

Cast iron contains a considerable amount of impurities. The chief impurity is carbon, which enters the iron from the coke. The amount of carbon in cast iron varies from 2 to 4¼ percent. There are also some silicon (about 2½ percent), some phosphorus, some sulfur, and a few other things.

Cast iron is strong and hard and is also the cheapest form of iron. It is used for objects that will have to bear steady pressure, such as weight, but won't have to stand sudden blows. Cast iron is brittle, and a sudden blow might shatter it.

If cast iron is heated with more iron ore and limestone, the impurities are removed, and almost pure iron is obtained. This is called *wrought iron*. Wrought iron is softer than cast iron, but it is tough; that is, it will take sudden shocks and blows without breaking. Cast iron was only formed after coke was produced. Using coke as fuel made it possible to produce temperatures high enough to melt the iron and mix it with carbon. In the Middle Ages when wood fires were used, the lower temperature produced wrought iron only.

The most useful, hardest, and strongest form of iron is a compromise between cast iron and wrought iron; that is, it contains some carbon but not as much carbon as cast iron does. Iron that contains between 0.15 and 1.5 percent carbon is called *steel*.

There are several ways of making steel. One way is to heat cast iron in special furnaces called *Bessemer converters* (named after the British inventor) and burn out the impurities. It is particularly important to manage things so that the sulfur and phosphorus are removed. After this has been done, certain impurities (carbon and often other elements) are put back in.

Steel has an advantage over other forms of iron in that we can make it stronger, harder, and tougher by *tempering* it—that is, by heating it to a red heat and then plunging it into cold water. The special characteristics of a piece of steel depend on the way in which it has been tempered and also on the quantity of carbon it contains. If the carbon content is less than one-fifth of 1 percent, the steel is *mild steel;* this is much like wrought iron and, because it is less expensive, has replaced wrought iron for most uses. *Structural steel,* which contains from one-fifth to three-fifths of 1 percent carbon, is stronger and can be used for beams in skyscrapers and bridges. *Tool steel,* which contains from 1 to 1.5 percent carbon, is stronger still.

The properties of steel also depend upon what other elements are added and how much. There are hundreds of different combinations of elements in steel. Alloys, in fact, are divided into two groups: *ferrous alloys,* which contain iron, and *non-ferrous alloys,* which do not. Iron, you see, is the key element. (The word "ferrous" comes from "ferrum," which is the Latin word for iron.)

The United States produces over a hundred million tons of steel a year. The automobile industry uses about a fifth of this. Railroads, buildings, and machinery take up much of the rest.

So much steel is used today that some people say we aren't in the Iron Age any more but in the *Steel Age*.

As an example of the way in which steel has revolutionized human life, consider buildings. Buildings made out of wood, brick, or even stone can be only a few stories high. If they are built too high, the weight above collapses the foundations. Nowadays, however, the "skeleton" of buildings is first constructed out of steel beams and pillars, and it is these steel pieces that bear the weight of the building. Steel is so strong that skyscrapers with a hundred stories can be built. Outside the steel skeleton, brick and stone can be used freely since they don't support the main weight. Since World War II there has been a fad for making the "skin" of skyscrapers out of aluminum and glass to give the buildings a light and airy appearance.

Steel is not only strong, but also elastic; that is, it gives with pressure, then springs back when the pressure is relaxed. In this way, skyscrapers can withstand artillery bombardment and earthquake shocks that would destroy smaller buildings built without steel. It is steel that makes suspension bridges possible as well as many other great engineering achievements of man.

In short, when strength is the main requirement, there is no substitute for steel.

RUST AND MAGNETISM

It is a pity that iron, the cheapest and strongest metal, should have any shortcomings, but it does. It has a most serious one: it combines with oxygen. This combination may be rapid, or it may be slow.

If iron is divided into small pieces (usually referred to as *iron filings*) and strongly heated, the pieces will combine with oxygen rapidly and produce enough heat to throw off white-hot sparks of glowing iron. (The *sparklers* you may have seen at Independence Day celebrations are made up of iron powder packed about a wire. The flame of a match is just barely hot enough to start such sparklers going. Once started, though, they go on furiously till all the iron has combined with oxygen.)

The serious shortcoming, however, is iron's slow combination with oxygen in the presence of moisture. This slow combination is called *rusting*. Iron unites with oxygen and water to form a *hydrated iron oxide,* the molecule of which contains iron atoms, oxygen atoms, and hydrogen atoms. This is *iron rust,* and we are all familiar with its appearance.

Iron rust, unfortunately, is a crumbly sort of substance that flakes away from the metal. It doesn't protect iron the way aluminum oxide protects aluminum. Instead, by flaking away, it always exposes fresh iron to the oxygen and moisture of the air. This fresh iron rusts and flakes away in its turn. Eventually the entire piece of iron rusts away.

It is for this reason that iron and most forms of steel must be painted before use. The layer of paint protects the metal from oxygen and moisture. Perhaps you have noted that steel used in construction always looks orange-red. The color is not rust, but paint.

Although it costs about a billion dollars a year to protect the world's iron from rusting or to replace iron that has rusted, the iron oxide that composes rust is not all bad. For instance, iron oxides, mixed with aluminum shavings, form *thermite*. The aluminum reacts with the iron oxide, once the mixture is heated to start it going. The reaction liberates great heat, with temperatures of nearly 3000 degrees C. being reached. Thermite can be used to weld metals (steel rails, for instance) without the use of torches. While the thermite is reacting, the aluminum atoms attach themselves to the oxygen atoms of the iron oxide, leaving behind a bit of unusually pure metallic iron.

Another peculiar property of iron is its ability to be attracted by a *magnet* and its ability to be a magnet. Magnetism is a kind of energy that always occurs together with electricity (which is another kind of energy). Any wire through which electricity is flowing behaves like a magnet; that is, the wire will attract small pieces of iron. (Why iron is more attracted by a magnet than any other element is still something of a mystery.)

If the wire through which electricity flows is wound into a coil, the magnetism of each turning of wire reinforces that of the neighboring turnings, so that the magnetism of the coiled wire is greater than that of the same wire drawn out straight. If the wire is wound round an iron core, the iron concentrates the magnetism somehow, and a powerful *electromagnet* results.

The magnetism is strongest at the ends, or *poles*, of the iron core, and pieces of iron and steel are strongly attracted toward those ends. A big electromagnet, when the current is flowing through its coil, can lift tons of iron and steel. Suppose we want to load iron and steel scrap into freight cars. We do it with an electromagnet that is hung from a crane. We lower the magnet onto the scrap, turn on the current, and lift a few tons of the scrap. Then we swing the load over a freight car and turn off the current. The magnet stops being a magnet, and the scrap falls into the freight car.

Most substances are affected by magnetism in one way or another, but usually the effects are very small. It is as if the atoms of those substances behaved like tiny magnets. Under ordinary conditions, these atomic magnets point every which way, and their energies cancel one another out.

The presence of an electric current and the resulting magnetism, however, cause the atoms (and iron atoms much
more than any others) to line up all in the same direction.
All the little magnetisms add up to a big magnetism. When
the electricity is turned off, the atomic magnets drift every
which way again. Iron thus forms a *temporary magnet*.

Most forms of steel behave differently. Apparently the
atoms can't move about as easily in steel as in iron. Once
they are lined up properly, they stay that way even after
the electricity is turned off. Steel forms a *permanent magnet*.
The "horseshoe magnets" children play with are made of
steel. Many elements are weakly magnetic. They are said
to be *paramagnetic*. The strong magnetism of iron (and a
very few other metals) is much more dramatic. Iron is said
to be *ferromagnetic*.

The iron ore called magnetite or loadstone is a naturally
magnetic substance. It was first noticed that this black rock
attracted iron objects in a district of ancient Greece called
Magnesia. That is how magnetite and magnetism got their
names. The ancient Greeks were much impressed by loadstone and told all sorts of exaggerated tales about it. In the
Arabian Nights, too, there is a very tall tale: a loadstone
mountain is so powerful that ships have to stay far away
from it, as otherwise all their nails are drawn out and
pulled, kerplunk, to the mountain, leaving the ship a dis-
organized mess of loose timbers.

Our whole planet is a kind of magnet, and the *compass*
is a device that takes advantage of that fact. The compass
contains a magnetized steel needle, capable of turning
freely. It points to the earth's magnetic poles and so always
lines up in a certain direction (which, on most of the earth's
surface, is approximately north and south).

GOBLINS AND DEVILS

There are two elements, closely resembling iron, that seem to have bothered German miners considerably in the old days. When the miners came across ores containing these elements, they got into trouble. The ores didn't behave right. When treated in the usual ways, they didn't give familiar metals like iron, silver, and copper.

Some of the miners apparently decided that goblins dwelling in the earth had bewitched these ores. The German name for earth goblins, "Kobold," has come down to us in our name for element No. 27, *cobalt*. The other ore the miners called "Kupfer-nickel," which means "devil's copper" (the devil, after all, is sometimes called Old Nick in our own language and the "copper" was added to the name, because this particular nickel ore was reddish in color.) This was shortened to *nickel* and is the name now given to element No. 28. Cobalt was first isolated by Georg Brandt (not the Brand who discovered phosphorus) in 1735 and nickel by Axel Fredric Cronstedt in 1751.

Iron itself does a little fooling, too. The common mineral **iron pyrites** has a molecule containing one atom of iron and two of sulfur. It forms glistening yellowish crystals that have fooled many an amateur prospector and has therefore received the rather bitter name *fool's gold*.

Both nickel and cobalt usually occur along with iron. Nickel is the commoner of the two. More than 3 percent of the weight of the earth is nickel, and only one-fourth of 1 percent is cobalt. Most of this is in the earth's core (which is 90 percent iron and 10 percent nickel and is usually referred to as the *nickel-iron core*), both metals being less common in the earth's crust.

Both cobalt and nickel are about 10 percent heavier than iron and somewhat harder than iron. If they were as common as iron, they might even be more useful since, unlike iron, they rust very slowly.

Nickel, in fact, can protect metals against rust. A piece of metal (usually iron or copper) is put into a solution containing a nickel compound. If now, under the proper conditions, a current of electricity is run through the solution, nickel atoms come out of the solution and bind themselves to the piece of iron or copper. After a while the iron or copper is covered with a thin, solid film of *nickel plate*. The nickel has a pleasant, shiny appearance and protects the metal beneath from rusting. This process is called *electroplating*.

Both cobalt and nickel are attracted by a magnet—less strongly than iron, but more strongly than any other element. If nickel or cobalt is mixed with iron in certain proportions, the alloy that results makes a stronger magnet than iron alone. *Permalloy*, for instance, is about two-thirds nickel and one-third iron. This makes a stronger permanent magnet than ordinary steel does. Still stronger permanent magnets are made of *Alnico*, which contains both nickel and cobalt, and aluminum, too, mixed with steel. Recent research is concentrating on tiny grains of iron embedded in plastic, rather than on solid chunks of metal. In addition to being the strongest magnets yet, such powder magnets are easily shaped and molded since the plastic containing the grains is quite soft.

Nickel steels (containing about 3½ percent nickel) are particularly tough and are used in quantity. Most of the nickel produced goes into steel. One odd variety of nickel steel is *Invar*, which is five-eighths iron and three-eighths nickel. Metals expand slightly as temperature goes up and contract as it goes down. Invar is unusual in this respect. It expands or contracts only a fifteenth as much as ordinary steel does. This makes it particularly useful for objects that are expected to keep their size steady, such as measuring tapes and clock pendulums.

Cobalt is harder than nickel (which is harder than iron), and cobalt alloys (called *stellites*) are among the hardest alloys known. They stay hard even at quite high temperature and are therefore used in metal-cutting tools. The heat caused by the friction of cutting metal doesn't ruin stellite as it would most steels.

You may remember, from Chapter 2, that hydrogen hardens and solidifies plant oils into useful fats (see page 38). If hydrogen were just mixed with the oil, the change would take a long time. If certain metal powders are added to the mixture, the process is tremendously quickened. This metal powder, by hastening the process, acts as a *catalyst*. The cheapest catalyst for the purpose, and the one used in industry, is powdered nickel.

Certain cobalt compounds have a rather romantic use. When dry, they are blue. When exposed to moisture, however, their molecules attach water molecules to themselves, and the color changes to a pale pink. If these cobalt compounds are dissolved in water, a pale pink solution results. This solution can be used as a kind of "invisible ink" since the pale pink marks can hardly be seen even after the water evaporates. If the paper is gently heated, however, the water molecules attached to the cobalt compound are driven off. The "invisible ink" turns dark blue and becomes quite visible.

There is a more important use for this phenomenon. Silica gel, you may remember, is used as a desiccant (see page 85). Silica gel is a glassy, colorless substance, and the trouble is that you can't tell by looking at it whether it is used up or not. It may be holding all the water it can, and it may no longer be able to dry the air passing through it, and you can't tell. So cobalt compounds are added to it. When the silica gel is dry, it is blue because of the dry cobalt compound. As it gets used up and absorbs more and more water, it slowly turns pink because the cobalt compound combines with water and turns pink. In this way we build in a kind of moisture indicator and know when to replace our silica gel.

This also explains the working of various novelties that are supposed to predict rain or fair weather as some object turns pink or blue. A great deal of moisture in the air, which will turn a cobalt compound pink, will usually mean that it is likely to rain.

There is another association of cobalt and the color blue. Added to glass or ceramics, cobalt compounds will impart a beautiful deep blue color. The result is known as *cobalt glass*.

In recent years it has been found that *vitamin B_{12}*, a substance necessary to life in very small quantities, contains an atom of cobalt in its molecule. For this reason, vitamin B_{12} and similar compounds are called the *cobalamins*. Cobalt is therefore one of the *essential trace elements* in living tissue. By "trace" we mean "present in very small amounts."

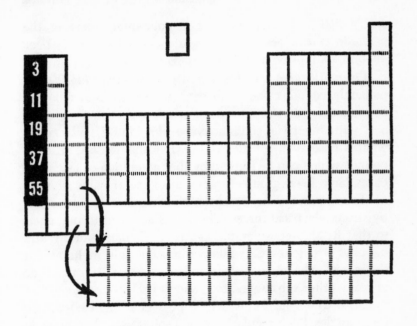

CHAPTER 12

Sodium and Potassium

THE ACTIVE ELEMENTS

DIVORCE BY ELECTRICITY

By 1800, chemists suspected that there were such elements as *sodium*, element No. 11, and *potassium*, element No. 19, but it was rather difficult to get them out into the open where they could be seen.

Actually, sodium and potassium are very common elements. A little over 2½ percent of the earth's crust is sodium, and a little under 2½ percent is potassium. Some of the common substances I have already discussed in this book contain sodium or potassium atoms.

Ordinary *table salt*, for instance, is *sodium chloride*. Its molecule contains one atom each of sodium and chlorine. Sodium chloride can be formed when hydrochloric acid reacts with the base, sodium hydroxide (and I will explain what a base is in a little while). For this reason, all compounds which can be formed by the interaction of acids and bases have been grouped under the general name of *salts*.

The atoms in salts are held together in a regular order by strong electrical forces. The atoms are hard to pull apart so that it takes considerable heat to melt most salts. Water melts at 0 degrees C. while sodium chloride melts at 801 degrees C. The regular arrangement of atoms in salts (and in many other substances, too) shows itself in the geometric shapes of the solid forms, which possess straight edges and sharp angles. Such regularly shaped solids are called *crystals*. Crystals of sodium chloride are cubic in shape.

Niter, or Chile saltpeter, is *sodium nitrate*, with a molecule containing one atom of sodium, one of nitrogen and three of oxygen. Ordinary glass is mostly *sodium silicate*, with a rather complicated molecule containing sodium, silicon and oxygen atoms.

Potassium occurs in ordinary saltpeter, which is *potassium nitrate* (one atom of potassium, one of nitrogen and three of oxygen). It occurs also in feldspar and mica. Potassium nitrate is used in making gunpowder. Sodium nitrate can't be used because it absorbs water on damp days and this would ruin the powder since damp gunpowder will not explode. Potassium nitrate, which does not absorb water so easily, is formed in decaying animal wastes, and before the days of modern chemistry, stables and cellars were regularly searched by governments for the precious crystals that would keep their soldiers shooting.

Both sodium and potassium compounds occur plentifully in sea water and in living tissue, too. Both are essential to life. Of the human body, 0.35 percent is potassium and 0.15 percent is sodium.

Most of the dissolved material in sea water is sodium chloride, of course (as you can guess if you have ever tasted the ocean while bathing in it). Fully 3 percent of the world's oceans are sodium chloride. Seas without an outlet may have much more. The Dead Sea, which separates Israel and Jordan, is 20 percent sodium chloride. There are vast "salt mines" in many places, where shallow arms of the sea have dried up completely, leaving their salt behind to be overlaid with rock and soil. Sometimes the salt layer is over half a mile thick. Since salt is not only necessary in the human diet, but is used for a thousand purposes in industry, such mines are important. (In the old days, the Russian government used to send political prisoners to work in salt mines in Siberia. We still use the phrase "back to the salt mines" to mean returning to any tiresome or unpleasant job.)

Yet despite the commonness of sodium and potassium compounds, the elements themselves are difficult to obtain. They are so active that they hold on tightly to the other atoms in the compounds and are difficult to pry loose.

It wasn't till 1807 that the British chemist Davy found out how to pry them loose. He did this by melting a suitable sodium or potassium compound and running an electric current through the hot liquid. Under the influence of the electric current, the sodium atom (or potassium atom) traveled to one end of the container while the other atom or atoms in the compound traveled to the other end.

In this way, sodium and potassium were separated out

of their compounds. They turned out to be silvery-white metals that are soft enough to be cut with a dull knife. Both melt at quite low temperatures, below the temperature of boiling water, in fact. Sodium melts at 98 degrees centigrade and potassium at 63 degrees.

Both are extremely active, potassium even more so than sodium. Once they have been separated as elements, the first thing they do is to try to get back into compounds. If a piece of sodium or potassium is exposed to air, it combines instantly with oxygen. The compound that is formed has no metallic luster; the shininess of the metal disappears at once when it is exposed. It *tarnishes*. Potassium combines with oxygen so energetically that a small piece will develop enough heat to melt and then burst into flame.

For this reason, if you should want to keep sodium or potassium more or less permanently, you had better place it under kerosene.

You might wonder if it wouldn't do just as well to keep the sodium or potassium under water. The answer to that is *for heaven's sake, no!* Sodium and potassium are so eager to combine with oxygen that they will pull the water molecule apart to get at the oxygen in it. One of the hydrogen atoms in the water molecule is turned loose as a result.

This means that if a small piece of sodium or potassium is dropped into water, there is a mad hiss as the liberated hydrogen comes off all about it. The sodium or potassium is thrown about forcefully, spinning and melting. The heat of the reaction is such that the hydrogen almost always catches fire.

In college organic chemistry laboratories, where sodium is often used, students must take particular precautions against starting a "sodium fire." The danger of such a fire is that it is difficult to put out. The first impulse is to pour water on it, but that, of course, would just make the situation worse.

Sodium is used in the laboratory when we want to get rid of small quantities of water. Certain chemical reactions will take place in ether that has no water at all in it. Even a tiny trace of water would spoil the reaction; yet ordinary ether, as it comes out of a can, generally has considerable water dissolved in it.

To remove water from the ether, we put a piece of sodium into a hollow cylinder that has a hole in the bottom. We then push a piston into the cylinder and squeeze it down tightly with a lever. Under the pressure, the soft sodium squirts out of the bottom hole, like toothpaste out of a tube, and is caught in the flask of ether. The flask is then stoppered, and the sodium is allowed to work. It won't react with the ether, but it combines with any water present, and tiny bubbles of hydrogen appear. When the bubbles stop, the water is all gone; the ether may be poured off and used.

Sodium is also used in *sodium vapor lamps*. Here a little sodium is added to the neon in the lamp. When the electricity passes through the neon, the sodium is vaporized and gives off a strong yellow glow that shows much farther through fog than the light of ordinary lamps.

THE OPPOSITE OF ACID

Many sodium compounds are familiar and useful. One that is useful but not very familiar is *sodium peroxide*. It is formed when sodium burns and its molecule contains two sodium atoms and two oxygen atoms. Like ozone or hydrogen peroxide, it can be used to bleach various materials, but it also has a more glamorous use. It combines with the carbon and one of the oxygen atoms of carbon dioxide, allowing the second oxygen atom to go free. Exhaled air, which is forced through canisters of sodium peroxide, has its carbon dioxide replaced by oxygen. The air is thus freshened and renewed. Sodium peroxide therefore comes in handy in enclosed places where the air supply is limited and must be used over and over, as in submarines.

When sodium liberates hydrogen from the water molecule, it hangs on to the oxygen atom and to one of the hydrogens. The compound that is formed is *sodium hydroxide,* with a molecule consisting of one atom each of sodium, oxygen, and hydrogen.

Sodium hydroxide, as I mentioned a bit earlier, belongs to a class of compounds called *bases*. Where acid molecules hold hydrogen atoms loosely and give them up easily, basic molecules snatch up hydrogen atoms. Thus, the properties of bases are the opposite of the properties of acids. If a base is added to an acid, they neutralize each other. The mixture is a much weaker chemical than either one separately. It is often useful to be able to neutralize acids, but sodium hydroxide is sometimes a bit too strong for convenience.

Sodium hydroxide is the cheapest and most important strong base and is of great use industrially. The way it is made is to run an electric current through a water solution of sodium chloride. The chlorine atom is forced to one end and liberated. The sodium atom, however, isn't liberated. If it were, it would just react with the water to release hydrogen and form sodium hydroxide. It is hydrogen that is liberated in the first place, then, and sodium hydroxide is left behind in solution.

Sodium hydroxide will split molecules of fats and oils

into *glycerol* and *fatty acids*. Sodium atoms combine with the fatty acids to form *soap*. In peacetime it is the soap that is the important product of this process. In wartime, however, it is the glycerol that is important, for out of it explosives can be made. During World War II, people were asked to save their bacon fat and gravy drippings and turned them into the butcher for collection, just for the sake of the glycerol.

This ability of sodium hydroxide to split fat molecules is useful in another way. If some sodium hydroxide is poured into sink drains that are clogged with solidified grease, it can dissolve the grease or at least break it up a little and allow water to flush through again. Sodium hydroxide used for this purpose is usually called by its older name, *lye*. It is sometimes called *caustic soda*, the word "caustic" meaning "biting," the effect of the chemical on skin.

Large quantities of sodium hydroxide are used in the conversion of wood pulp to rayon or paper. If cotton fibers are treated with sodium hydroxide, the cotton becomes silkier, stronger and more easily dyed. This was discovered by an Englishman named John Mercer in 1850, and cotton so treated is now called *mercerized cotton*.

A weaker base is *sodium carbonate*, with a molecule containing two atoms of sodium, one of carbon, and three of oxygen. When it reacts with acids, carbon and oxygen atoms break away and are given off as carbon dioxide. A common name for sodium carbonate is simply *soda*. This was the name given to sodium carbonate long before people knew of the atoms that make it up or even that there are atoms. The name of the element sodium was derived from "soda" because sodium is contained in soda.

Sodium carbonate is often used as a source of carbon

dioxide—in fire extinguishers, for instance, as we saw in Chapter 5. Carbon dioxide produced from sodium carbonate can also be dissolved in water to produce *soda water*. If flavors are added, we have *soda pop*. These are poor names since there is no soda in soda water or soda pop, but it is far too late to do anything about them.

Sodium carbonate is still too strong a base for some purposes. A still weaker base is *sodium bicarbonate*, which has only one sodium atom in its molecule. (The second sodium atom is replaced by a hydrogen atom in sodium bicarbonate.) Sodium bicarbonate also reacts with acids to form carbon dioxide, and it is so gentle a base that it can be taken internally for "gas pains" following overeating. You may have heard the compound referred to, in an offhand way, as "bicarb."

In the stomach, sodium bicarbonate neutralizes some of the acid that is always present there. The carbon dioxide produced forces its way out of the stomach as a belch and usually carries other gases with it. This relieves the pressure that may have been causing the pain.

Sodium bicarbonate is also used in baking. When it is combined with some sort of weak acid (sour milk, for example) in the batter, it produces carbon dioxide, which, as we saw in Chapter 5, puffs up the batter and makes the cake light and fluffy. For this reason, a common name for sodium bicarbonate is *baking soda*, and baking powders usually contain some.

Sodium sulfate (with a molecule containing a sodium atom, a sulfur atom and four oxygen atoms, plus ten water molecules loosely attached) was first studied by the German chemist, Johann Rudolf Glauber, in 1658 and is commonly called *Glauber's salt* in consequence. When Glauber's salt dissolves in water, the temperature of the water drops considerably. Now usually, adding chemicals to water will heat it. Sulfuric acid or sodium hydroxide will heat water to boiling if dissolved quickly and in large amounts. That, somehow, is what the chemist grows to expect. Water that turns icy as a chemical is added is startling.

Potassium compounds behave much like sodium compounds but are usually rarer. There is less potassium in the soil than sodium, in the first place, and some of the potassium is in a form that is not easy to get at.

The best source of easy-to-get potassium compounds is the Stassfurt deposit, located in Germany, where a dried-up arm of the sea has apparently deposited substances that include considerable quantities of various potassium compounds.

Potassium salts are more soluble than sodium chloride, and that ancient sea happened to dry up slowly in such a way that the sodium chloride was deposited first while enough water was left to keep the potassium salts in solution. The potassium compounds came out of the thick brine only at the end. They spread out on the top of the earlier deposits and were therefore easy to get at, and in fairly pure form at that. More than one-third of the world's production of potassium is from these deposits.

Before World War I, German chemistry was the best-developed in the world, and German chemists were always using potassium compounds for one purpose or another since these were fairly cheap in Germany. Potassium compounds were by no means so cheap elsewhere, but for quite a while chemists in other countries, such as Great Britain and the United States, followed the Germans blindly, using potassium compounds when sodium compounds were much cheaper and would often (but not always) have done just as well. This shows that scientists, too, have their human failings.

Plants need considerable potassium, and there is danger that the soil will run short of potassium and lose fertility. Many fertilizers contain potassium atoms in their molecules for this reason. (Originally, the potassium salts of the Stassfurt deposits were thrown away while the miners concentrated on the sodium chloride beneath. It wasn't until 1865 that the Germans recognized the fertilizing value of the material they had been calling "Abraumsalze" which in English means "waste salt.")

Plants use potassium in such quantities, indeed, that they were once used as the source of potassium compounds. (In fact, it wasn't until 1797 that potassium compounds were discovered in minerals. Until then, they had only been known to occur in plants.) Plants were burned, and the potassium compounds left behind in the ash were dissolved out in water. The water was then poured into large iron pots and boiled away. *Potassium carbonate* (with a molecule composed of two atoms of potassium, one of carbon, and three of oxygen) was left behind. (In some ocean plants, it is sodium carbonate that occurs in the ash and it, too, was prepared in this fashion before the days of modern chemistry.)

The common name for potassium carbonate was potash (obviously because it was the ash left behind in the pot). Sodium carbonate, when prepared this way, was similarly called *soda ash*. *Potassium hydroxide*, which closely resembles sodium hydroxide in its behavior, but is more expensive, is called *caustic potash*. It is from the word "potash" that the element potassium gets its name. The Arabic word for this ash is "al-quili," and from that potassium hydroxide and sodium hydroxide received the name of *caustic alkalis*. What's more, sodium and potassium, as well as other elements in the same column of the periodic table, are called *alkali metals*. (During the Middle Ages, the Arabs did considerable chemical work of a primitive kind, and a number of Arabic words are still used in modern chemistry.)

You're probably familiar with the word "alkali." In making soap, it is always necessary to get rid of any extra sodium hydroxide that may be present, as otherwise the soap would be very irritating to the skin. People who advertise soap on radio or television are always saying, therefore, that their soap contains "no harsh alkali." It is also common to say that a substance is *alkaline* when you want to say that it is basic—that is, the opposite of acid.

Soap, by the way, was not known in ancient times. The Greeks and Romans, however, found that wood ashes had cleansing properties. This was because of the potassium carbonate in it, which splits the molecules of grease and oil as sodium or potassium hydroxide would do, though not as well.

DISCOVERY BY LIGHT

The alkali metals other than sodium and potassium are quite rare. The simplest is *lithium*, element No. 3. It is just above sodium in the periodic table. It is the lightest metal of all, just half as heavy as water. This means that it is lighter than most kinds of wood. It is less than a fifth as heavy as aluminum.

Its lightness doesn't do us much good, though. Not only is it rare, but, like all alkali metals, it is very reactive. If exposed to air, it will even combine with the nitrogen in it, which the other alkali metals won't do. Small quantities, however, may be added to certain alloys to make them harder. *Lithium nitrate* is sometimes added to fireworks to produce a red light.

New uses have been found in recent years. Lithium hydride (with a molecule containing one atom of lithium and one of hydrogen) is probably used in some kinds of hydrogen bombs. A more pleasant use is as a catalyst (see page 147) in new processes for making new varieties of plastics.

Lithium was first discovered by August Arfvedson in 1817. It was isolated by Davy, in 1818, by the electrical procedure that worked for sodium and potassium. The name of the element comes from the Greek word for "stone," because it occurred in the mineral kingdom only, whereas sodium and potassium (the only other alkali metals known at the time) occurred in plants and animals as well.

The heavy alkali metals, *rubidium*, element No. 37, and *cesium*, element No. 55, were discovered in an interesting fashion. You may remember (page 52) that an element, if heated, will give off light, that this light, if passed through a prism, will break up into lines of various colors, and that each element has its own set of lines. Sodium, for instance, or a compound containing sodium, will give off two strong yellow lines when heated. This form of analysis is called *spectroscopy*, and it was by this method, as we saw, that helium was discovered in the sun.

Helium was not the first element discovered by spectroscopy. A German chemist, R. W. Bunsen, and a German physicist, G. R. Kirchhoff, were studying the lines produced by various heated substances. In 1860 they came across a substance that produced blue lines that didn't duplicate the lines of any other element. From the chemical behavior of the substance they knew its molecule must contain atoms of an alkali metal. This one must be a new alkali metal, hitherto unknown. They called that metal cesium after the

Latin word for "sky-blue." Cesium was the first element to be discovered by the kind of light it produced.

Shortly after, Bunsen and Kirchoff found a substance containing still another alkali metal type of atom. This time, red lines were produced; so they called the new metal rubidium after the Latin word for "deep red."

It was quite a while, of course, before either element was isolated as the pure metal. Cesium wasn't isolated until 1882 and rubidium until 1910. Both were obtained by use of Davy's electrophoresis method.

Cesium is the softest metal (it is as soft as wax) and the most active. It melts at a temperature of only 28.5 degrees centigrade. Since this is only 83 degrees Fahrenheit, you can see that cesium is a liquid on any hot summer day.

Elements when heated can be made to give off some of the tiny electrons (which I mentioned in the introduction to this book) that make up the outer portions of their atoms. Of all the elements, cesium can be made to give up electrons with the least trouble. Scientists speculate that in the future it may be possible to propel vessels through space by firing electrons away from matter. This method of space-ship propulsion is called an *ion drive*. Cesium may then be the "fuel" used and this rare metal may turn out to be an important substance of the space age.

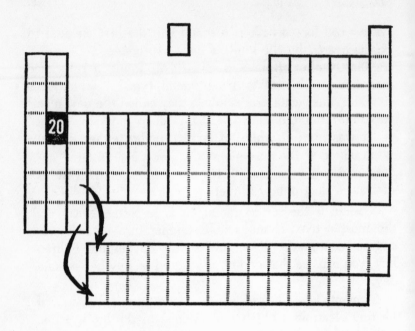

CHAPTER 13 **Calcium**

THE ELEMENT OF BONE

FROM CHALK TO PEARLS

There are some minerals in the earth's crust that aren't silicates. The commonest of them is *limestone*. This mineral is known by several names according to the form in which it is found. When it occurs in opaque crystals, it is called *calcite;* when it occurs in transparent crystals, it is called *Iceland spar.* A very attractive form of limestone is *marble,*

162

which can take a high polish and out of which the ancient Greeks and Romans built beautiful temples. Finally, in its rather crumbly, dull form, limestone is called *chalk*, as in the famous chalk cliffs of Dover.

The chemical name of limestone is *calcium carbonate,* and, as the name shows, it contains atoms of an element I have not yet discussed. This element is *calcium*, No. 20. It is a silvery-white metal, very reactive, but not as reactive as the alkali metals discussed in the previous chapter. It reacts with water, releasing hydrogen, but does so less vigorously than sodium or potassium. It tarnishes rapidly in air as it combines with the oxygen and also with the nitrogen. Calcium was first isolated as the element in 1808 by Davy, who used the same electrical method that worked for sodium and potassium.

Calcium carbonate (its molecule contains one atom of calcium, one of carbon, and three of oxygen) is produced by many living organisms as a protective substance. Eggshells are made of calcium carbonate, and so are the shells of oysters and clams. When an irritating particle, such as a piece of sand, gets inside an oyster, the oyster may wall it off with calcium carbonate, forming a round, lustrous object we call a *pearl*. Perfectly shaped pearls can be very valuable, and yet they are only calcium carbonate, the same calcium carbonate you find in an eggshell.

Calcium carbonate reacts with acids, just as sodium carbonate does, and in doing so gives off carbon dioxide. It does this much more slowly than sodium carbonate because it does not dissolve in water, and sodium carbonate does. (Substances that dissolve engage in all sorts of chemical activity much more quickly and thoroughly than substances that do not dissolve.)

If a pearl is dropped into an acid solution (vinegar,

perhaps), it will slowly react with the acid; it will break up and be eaten away. That's one way to tell a real pearl from an imitation, but perhaps you wouldn't care to try such a test on any pearls of your own. If so, I don't blame you.

There is a variety of sea creatures called *corals*, which form calcium carbonate skeletons in different shapes, some of them quite fantastic and beautiful. They live in warm, shallow seas, and many of the reefs that exist in the South Pacific are nothing more than the accumulated skeletons of such animals.

The skeletons of microscopic creatures called *foraminifers* are also made of calcium carbonate, and the accumulated skeletons of trillions upon trillions of such animals may form tremendous piles. The famous *chalk* cliffs of Dover are composed of such skeletons. It is possible, in fact, that all the calcium carbonate deposits on earth may be the remains of various small animals. There is a great deal of it, too, for calcium atoms make up 3½ percent of the earth's crust.

Underground deposits of calcium carbonate are slowly affected by rainfall. Under the influence of the rainwater seeping down from the surface of the earth (and carrying with it carbon dioxide, which it had dissolved out of the air as it fell), the calcium carbonate molecule is altered. It adds on the atoms contained in water and carbon dioxide to become *calcium bicarbonate*, which is more soluble in water than calcium carbonate is.

Slowly the calcium bicarbonate is washed away by additional rain, and great hollows form underground. The Mammoth Cave in Kentucky and the Carlsbad Caverns in New Mexico are such *limestone caves*. They contain all sorts of weird and beautiful shapes of limestone as calcium bicarbonate collects wherever water (containing it in solution) drips. As the water evaporates, the calcium bicarbonate remains behind, loses water and carbon dioxide, and becomes calcium carbonate again. The limestone "icicles" suspended from the roof are called *stalactites*. The columns that build up from the floor are *stalagmites*.

LIME

If calcium carbonate is strongly heated, one atom of carbon and two of oxygen break away from the molecule and are given off as carbon dioxide. What is left behind is *calcium oxide*, with its molecule composed of one calcium atom and one oxygen atom.

A common name for this substance is *quicklime*. The syllable "quick" in the name doesn't mean that the substance is fast. "Quick" also means "alive," as in the phrase "the quick and the dead." Calcium oxide is considered to be "alive" because of the way in which it absorbs water. It does so very rapidly, giving off a great deal of heat in the process. In fact, calcium oxide to which water is added can develop enough heat to set wood on fire. (We already know how to start a fire by adding water to sodium or potassium. Now here is another way of starting a fire with water.)

People who worked with calcium oxide were struck by the "eagerness" with which it takes up water. It seemed to them that the substance behaved like a desperately thirsty man, and they began to call the process of adding water to lime "slaking," as though it were a question of slaking thirst. This habit of treating the procedure as though it were something lifelike resulted, finally, in the name "quicklime."

Calcium oxide is often called simply *lime*. The name "calcium" is derived from "calx," the Latin word for lime.

Calcium oxide is a kind of substance that chemists of an older day called an *earth*. These are high-melting oxides. Other examples which I have already mentioned are aluminum oxide, iron oxide, and silicon dioxide. When calcium oxide is treated with water, it forms *calcium hydroxide*, the common name for which is *slaked lime* (lime that is no longer thirsty). Calcium hydroxide is a base. Calcium oxide, therefore, since it gives rise to a base on solution in water, is called an *alkaline earth*. (I said in Chapter 12, remember, that "alkaline" and "base" are both words that mean the opposite of "acid.") For this reason, calcium and elements similar to it are called the *alkaline earth metals*.

Calcium oxide melts at the high temperature of 2,500 degrees centigrade. If a flame plays upon calcium oxide, it won't melt (unless the flame is of the very hottest kind) but will glow with an intense white brilliance. This light was sometimes used (in the days before electric lighting) to illuminate a theatrical stage. People who are, for one reason or another, on show before the general public are still said to be "in the limelight."

SUBSTANCES THAT SET

In some ways, calcium hydroxide is a stronger base than sodium or potassium hydroxide. An ounce of calcium hydroxide will neutralize nearly 10 percent more acid than an ounce of sodium hydroxide will. It will neutralize 50 percent more acid than an ounce of potassium hydroxide will. Here again, however, the solubility has to be considered.

You all know that some substances dissolve in water. The salt you add to your soup dissolves. So does the sugar you add to your coffee. Other substances, such as sand, glass, and calcium carbonate, do not dissolve in water.

Sodium hydroxide and potassium hydroxide are very soluble. A quart of water will dissolve a pound or more of sodium hydroxide and at least two pounds of potassium hydroxide. With all that base in them, such solutions are *strongly basic*.

Calcium hydroxide is only slightly soluble. A quart of water will dissolve only 1/400 ounce of calcium hydroxide. For that reason, a solution of calcium hydroxide (commonly called *limewater*) is only *weakly basic*. The calcium hydroxide is strong enough, but there isn't much of it there.

Carbon dioxide will react with even the small amount of calcium hydroxide in limewater and in doing so will form calcium carbonate. Calcium carbonate is even less soluble than calcium hydroxide. As it is formed by the action of carbon dioxide on limewater, it comes out of solution (that is, it is *precipitated*) in the form of a white powder. If you were to blow your breath through a straw dipped into limewater, you would soon turn the liquid milky with precipitated calcium carbonate.

This is an interesting way to show that there is carbon dioxide in the breath, and what happened between the carbon dioxide and the calcium hydroxide is also important in our everyday life.

Whitewash, for instance, is powdered calcium hydroxide stirred up in water. Some of it dissolves, but most of it just floats about in the water as a *suspension*. When the whitewash is smeared on a fence or some other wooden object, the thin layer of calcium hydroxide quickly reacts with the carbon dioxide of the air and becomes calcium carbonate. The calcium carbonate sticks firmly to the wood, and since it is insoluble, rain doesn't wash it away.

If calcium hydroxide is mixed with sand in the proper proportions, *mortar* is the result. Mortar is placed between bricks as the bricks are piled up to form a wall. Again exposure to the air changes the calcium hydroxide to calcium carbonate. In this way the mortar *sets;* that is, it becomes hard and sticks firmly to the bricks, making the brick wall all one piece, so to speak.

Builders sometimes need a substance that will set and harden under water. (Mortar won't do, for it needs air, with its carbon dioxide, in order to set.) The answer to that need is *cement.* Cement is a mixture of limestone and clay. When water is added, the limestone and clay combine with the water and with each other to form a hard *calcium aluminum silicate.*

Cement is useful for a number of purposes, but its most dramatic use is in the building of huge dams. That is just where its ability to harden under water is most valuable. To increase the strength of the cement, we mix it with sand and crushed stone. If the mixture, called *concrete,* is poured around a kind of skeleton of iron bars, it becomes *reinforced concrete,* and then it is strong enough to hold back whole rivers of water.

An interesting calcium compound is familiarly called *plaster of Paris.* Its more formal name is *calcium sulfate hemihydrate* (with a molecule containing one atom of calcium, one of sulfur, and four of oxygen—which makes calcium sulfate—plus a small amount of water, one water molecule for every two calcium sulfate molecules). When plaster of Paris is exposed to water, it changes to *gypsum,* or *calcium sulfate dihydrate,* which is a combination of two water molecules with every one calcium sulfate molecule. Plaster of Paris is a dry loose powder. As it changes to gypsum, it sets and becomes a hard, solid *cast.* Plaster of Paris is used for casts on broken limbs to keep the limbs motionless till the bones are repaired.

Gypsum, by the way, is a common naturally occurring mineral. Sometimes it is found in white masses known as *alabaster*. You are probably more familiar with it as the kind of blackboard chalk used in your schoolroom.

Another common calcium compound is *calcium chloride* (with a molecule containing one atom of calcium and two of chlorine). It absorbs water vapor from the air and for that reason is sometimes spread on dirt roads. Even in dry weather it absorbs enough water vapor from the air to keep the road surface moist. If the surface were allowed to dry completely, passing vehicles would raise clouds of dust, which would make driving uncomfortable and even dangerous.

WHEN SOAP DOESN'T WORK

A number of the compounds I mentioned earlier in this book contain calcium atoms in their molecules.

Bleaching powder, for instance (see page 90), is *calcium hypochlorite*. Fluorspar, the flux whose properties gave the element fluorine its name (see page 94), is *calcium fluoride*. Ordinary glass contains *calcium silicate* as well as sodium silicate. Sodium silicate, all by itself, is sometimes called *water glass* because it will dissolve in water, whereas the calcium silicate-sodium silicate mixture in glass will not. (We make glass, in fact, by heating sand, soda, and limestone to over 1,300 degrees centigrade and letting the mixture melt together. The sand supplies the silicate, the soda supplies the sodium, and the limestone supplies the calcium.) When potash replaces soda, the resulting *potash glass* is harder and higher melting than ordinary *soda glass*.

Ordinary glass doesn't have a perfectly smooth surface but has slight waves and ridges. Objects seen through such glass are distorted. If the surface is ground down and made even, the result is *plate glass,* and this is free of distortion.

If two layers of glass are held together by a thin sheet of transparent plastic, the glass is shatter-proof. The glass may still break, but the pieces won't go flying. They will remain in place, stuck to the plastic. Such *safety glass* is used in automobiles, for instance, so that in case of accident, the terrible damage that can be caused by flying glass is avoided.

Thin layers of glass coated over clay, brick or other high-melting substances are called *glaze.* Certain compounds can be added to the glaze to make it white and opaque, rather than transparent. Such an opaque glaze is an *enamel.* Much of the equipment in modern kitchens is of metal with an enamel coating. The metal supplies the strength, while the enamel provides protection against the action of air and water, while having a smooth beauty of its own.

Glass can take on another kind of beauty, too, when chemicals are added to give it color. Small pieces of differently colored *stained glass* of this sort can be put together to produce splendid works of art.

Calcium compounds are important for life as well as for glass. Many fertilizers are calcium compounds. Superphosphate, for instance, which I mentioned in Chapter 9, is a mixture of *calcium phosphate* and calcium sulfate. A mixture of *calcium nitrate* and calcium oxide is another important fertilizer.

Most important of all, bones contain calcium. I described bones earlier as being made up of a phosphate (see page 115). Actually, they are made up of a complex calcium phosphate mixed with a smaller quantity of calcium carbonate. The skeleton of the average adult male contains about two and a quarter pounds of calcium and only about one pound of phosphorus. Phosphorus is also important in the soft tissues of the body, but calcium occurs almost entirely in the bones. So it is calcium that has the best right to be called the "bone element."

So far, it certainly seems that calcium has only a good side and no bad side at all. Yet that is wrong. In one way, at least, calcium can be very annoying to the housewife.

The water that comes from your tap may be of the type that produces beautiful suds when soap is added. Such water contains only small amounts of solid matter dissolved in it. Water taken from mountain reservoirs, fed mostly by rain, is like this. Such water is called *soft water*. Among the fortunate cities that have soft water available for their population are Boston and New York.

Water taken from lakes and rivers has been in contact with the soil for some time. Often it has managed to dissolve a small quantity of calcium compounds. When soap is added to such water, the soap molecules combine with the calcium compounds to form *calcium soaps*. Calcium soaps don't form suds. They are sticky and insoluble. They settle out on clothes and in the wash basin and are hard to remove. Instead of cleaning, they make things appear dirtier. The "ring" around the bathtub, after a bath, is usually a collection of calcium soap rather than just dirt.

Water of this type is called *hard water*.

Fortunately, hard water can be softened. If the calcium compound that is present is calcium bicarbonate, just boiling the water is enough. The soluble calcium bicarbonate is converted to calcium carbonate, which, being insoluble, settles out. It is only the calcium compound in solution that does harm. With calcium carbonate out of solution, there is nothing left in the water to interfere with sudsing. Water of this type, which can be softened by boiling, is *temporary hard water*.

But what if the water contains calcium sulfate or calcium chloride? These are not affected by boiling. The water can be boiled as long as you like and yet remain hard. This is *permanent hard water*.

If sodium carbonate is added to permanent hard water, it combines with the calcium sulfate or calcium chloride to form calcium carbonate. The calcium carbonate settles out of the water and does no harm thereafter. The only thing left in the water is sodium sulfate or sodium chloride, which has no bad effect on soap. The sodium carbonate has softened the water, and for that reason it is frequently called *washing soda*. (Other substances, such as sodium phosphate and ammonia, can be added to hard water to get rid of calcium. They are water softeners also.)

We can also soften water by allowing it to pass through a certain type of clay called *zeolite*. The calcium atom combines with the zeolite as the water passes through, and harmless sodium atoms from the zeolite take its place in solution.

Chemists have put together complex organic molecules called *ion-exchange resins* that work still better than zeolite. We can even make ion-exchange resins that will take out all, or nearly all, the various substances dissolved in water, sodium chloride included. In this way, seawater, for instance, can be made drinkable. You can see what a useful substance such an ion-exchange resin would be on board a life raft floating on a lonely stretch of ocean with its occupants waiting for rescue.

Another way of getting round the problem of hard water is to manufacture compounds that behave like soap but don't form insoluble compounds with calcium. Many types of such *detergents* have been put on the market in the last ten years, and hard water is far less of a problem for the housewife than it used to be.

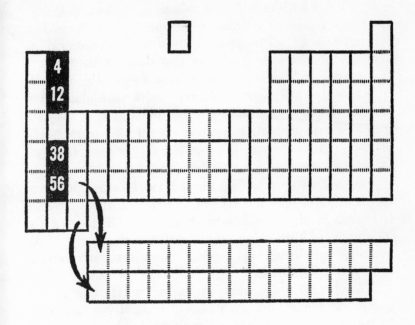

CHAPTER 14

Magnesium

THE INCENDIARY ELEMENT

THE WHITE FLAME

Just above calcium in the periodic table is element No. 12, *magnesium*. It closely resembles calcium in many of its properties and is almost as active as calcium. Magnesium is another of the metals first isolated by Davy (in 1808) with his method of electrical divorce.

When exposed to air, however, magnesium doesn't tarnish in the unsatisfactory way sodium, potassium, calcium, and iron do. Instead, it behaves like aluminum. It is quickly covered with a thin, transparent layer of magnesium oxide. This is so inert and so protective that sheets of magnesium can be used in building airplanes even though the element is very active. Magnesium is more active than aluminum; it is, in fact, the most active metal that can be built into manufactured products in pure or almost pure form. Magnesium, like aluminum, is protected by an inert layer of oxide (*magnesium oxide*, this time).

Magnesium must not be pushed too far, though. Even the oxide layer does not protect it perfectly. If magnesium is heated in air, it will burst into a white flame that is blindingly brilliant. Accidental friction may do the trick. Factories producing magnesium must take precautions against this fire hazard.

This bright magnesium flame, of course, like almost everything unpleasant, has its uses. When it was necessary to take a photograph without sunlight, in the days before highly sensitive films were developed, some other bright light had to be substituted. The magnesium flame was bright enough, and it is still often used in photography. At first photographers put some magnesium powder, plus a compound that gave off oxygen when heated, into a little open container and set it off at the right moment. This was crude and a little dangerous, too. Nowadays we have *flash bulbs*, which contain a network of fine magnesium wires (aluminum can be used, too) surrounded by oxygen. The camera may be built so that a small electric current ignites the magnesium just as the shutter is snapped and produces a bright, simultaneous flash. (Naturally, a flash bulb can be used only once.)

Magnesium fire has its wartime uses, too. The flares that are dropped by airplanes at night as signals or as devices to light up the ground and guide the bombs are usually burning magnesium.

Even more unpleasant are the *incendiary bombs,* which are usually devices for setting a quantity of magnesium on fire as soon as they strike their target. The heat of a magnesium fire is enough to set anything inflammable in a building to burning briskly. It is hard to put out a magnesium fire before great damage is done. Magnesium is so active that it will combine with nitrogen and will even pull oxygen out of carbon dioxide and water. None of these usually inert substances are inert enough to put out a magnesium fire. Sand, however, will do the job. That is why, during World War II, people were urged to have buckets of sand ready for use during air raids.

The most useful thing about magnesium, in a constructive way, is its lightness. It is even much lighter than aluminum. A cubic inch of aluminum, as I have said earlier, weighs one and a half ounces, but a cubic inch of magnesium weighs just under one ounce. For that reason, magnesium, like aluminum, is used in aircraft and in other structures wherever lightness is more important than strength. It is generally used in the form of an alloy with aluminum. Two such alloys are *Dowmetal,* which is 90 percent magnesium and the rest mostly aluminum, and *Magnalium,* which is 30 percent magnesium and the rest aluminum.

The use of light metal alloys for aircraft during World War II was so great that the world production of magnesium had to be increased tenfold, from 20,000 tons a year to more than 200,000 tons a year.

THE UNDERPINNING OF THE CONTINENTS

Magnesium is a common element of the earth's crust, making up 2½ percent of its weight and it gets still commoner as we burrow deeper.

On page 125, you may remember, I said that the continents are huge granite slabs, a mixture of silica and aluminum silicates. Underneath those granite slabs (and underneath the water of the ocean) is *basalt*, which is a *magnesium silicate*. Just as the continents make up the sial layer (an abbreviation for silicon and aluminum), the region beneath is called the *sima* layer (an abbreviation for silicon and magnesium). In the crust itself, magnesium carbonate, in combination with calcium carbonate, makes up whole mountain ranges. The combination is called *dolomite*.

If the entire earth, not just its crust, is taken into account, there is more magnesium than aluminum. Magnesium, in fact, makes up 8½ percent of the entire earth, with some geologists suggesting that the percentage may be as high as 17, and the only metal commoner than that is iron.

Some common types of magnesium silicate are asbestos and talc. *Asbestos* is a mineral that can be pulled apart into fibers that can actually be spun and woven into a very coarse kind of cloth. Curtains or articles of clothing made of such cloth will not burn and will also insulate against heat (or cold) for a time. Steam pipes and hot-water pipes are often wrapped in asbestos, and all sorts of fireproof roofing, tiles, and insulation are made of it. *Talc* is a soft, slick-to-the-feel substance, which in powdered form is used as the well-known talcum powder. Solid masses of talc are called *soapstone*. Still another form of magnesium silicate is *meerschaum*, a light, porous substance (the name is the German word meaning "sea-foam") used in making smokers' pipes. With use, the pores absorb the colored tobacco tars and the whole pipe takes on a rich color which is valued by those who are interested in such things.

Yet it is not from the soil that mankind is getting its magnesium these days. One of the solids dissolved in seawater is *magnesium chloride*. There is only one-fifth as much magnesium chloride as sodium chloride in the sea, but, even so, a cubic mile of seawater contains eighteen million tons of magnesium chloride. Since there are about three hundred million cubic miles of seawater altogether, we are in no danger of running out of magnesium if we can get it out of the sea. As a matter of fact, we can, and we do. Magnesium is the one metal we can obtain economically from the sea. The only other element we get from the sea is a non-metal, bromine (see page 98).

Magnesium chloride sometimes occurs in ordinary salt as an impurity. It doesn't do us any harm to eat it in small quantities, but it can be annoying in another way. Magnesium chloride, like calcium chloride, pulls water vapor out of the air. When it is present in salt, it attracts enough water to make the salt damp (especially on rainy days). The salt then cakes and won't pour freely. This is a small thing, but it can be awfully hard on the temper of the lady of the house. Many brands of salt sold these days are treated to prevent caking. Magnesium chloride also occurs in combination with potassium chloride in the Stassfurt deposits. This combination is called *carnallite*.

The common name for magnesium oxide is *magnesia*. This is named for the same district in Greece that gave the name to magnets and magnetism. It is from "magnesia" that the name of the element magnesium is derived. Magnesium oxide is refractory and melts at a very high temperature, even higher than the also refractory calcium oxide, and both are often used for furnace linings. A mixture of magnesium oxide and magnesium chloride, after wetting, sets into a hard mass in a few hours and is called *Sorel cement*.

When magnesium oxide is dissolved in water, it becomes *magnesium hydroxide*, which is basic and even less soluble in water than calcium hydroxide. When magnesium hydroxide is mixed with water, it forms a creamy white suspension called *milk of magnesia*. Milk of magnesia is sometimes used as an antacid and as a laxative. Two other magnesium compounds sometimes used as laxatives are *magnesium citrate* and *magnesium sulfate*.

Magnesium sulfate, when hooked up with seven water molecules for each magnesium sulfate molecule, is more commonly known as *Epsom salt*. It gets this name from the fact that it was first prepared from spring water found at the small town of Epsom, in southeastern England, back in 1695.

Magnesium compounds make water hard, as calcium compounds do. (So do iron compounds, by the way.) The same methods that soften water by getting rid of calcium compounds (see page 171) also do the trick for magnesium and iron.

Magnesium is another of the elements that are essential to life. There is about three-fourths of an ounce of it in the human body, most of it in the bones.

I have left for the last one thing about magnesium that is perhaps the most important of all. All green plants contain a compound known as *chlorophyll*. It is chlorophyll that traps the energy of sunlight and puts it to work so that the plant can manufacture all its tissues out of simple water, carbon dioxide, and minerals. It is on the plant tissues that all animals must live in the long run (see page 73). That means that all plant and animal life (and most microscopic forms of life, too) depend on chlorophyll. Well, each chlorophyll molecule contains one atom of magnesium. Without that magnesium atom, chlorophyll wouldn't work, and plant and animal life would die out.

FIREWORKS AND X-RAYS

The two alkaline-earth metals below calcium in the periodic table are considerably less common than either calcium or magnesium, but neither is exactly rare.

Element No. 38 is *strontium,* so called because a mineral containing it was first discovered (in 1790) in a lead mine near Strontian, in Scotland.

Element No. 56 is *barium.* This name was derived from the old name of the commonest mineral containing the barium atom. That mineral was once called *barytes,* and that name came from a Greek word meaning "heavy." Barite, as the mineral is now called, is very heavy for a rock, being twice as heavy as granite, and a common English name for it is *heavy spar.*

Both strontium and barium were isolated by Davy in 1808. Both metals resemble calcium in appearance and properties and are even more active. Barium powder will catch fire when exposed to air. Barium is the most active of the alkaline earth metals, and the one most like the alkali metals.

Barium has a very strong tendency to absorb and combine with oxygen and nitrogen, and so have other active metals—magnesium and cesium, for example. For this reason, a little pellet containing these three metals is introduced into radio tubes during their manufacture. After the air in a tube has been pulled out by a vacuum pump, there is still just a trace of air left. Just a trace, but enough to interfere with the tube's working. It is then that the little pellet of barium, magnesium, and cesium within the tube is heated electrically. It vaporizes and combines with the tiny bit of oxygen and nitrogen left behind by the vacuum pump. The mixture of metals and compounds settles on the inner surface of the tube as it cools, forming a bright mirror. You must have noticed that mirror if you have ever looked at a radio tube.

Compounds of both strontium and barium are used in fireworks and in flares. *Strontium nitrate* burns with a bright red color, *barium nitrate* with a bright green. Strontium hydroxide will combine with sugar forming insoluble *strontium saccharate*. It can be used to separate sugar from molasses. Once the strontium saccharate is separated out, the strontium portion is easily removed.

Barium hydroxide is the strongest base among all the alkaline earth hydroxides. In some ways, it has an advantage over sodium and potassium hydroxides. The latter absorb carbon dioxide from the air (unless special precautions are taken). The sodium and potassium carbonates that result make the hydroxides impure. Barium hydroxide also absorbs carbon dioxide but the barium carbonate that forms, unlike the alkali carbonates, is insoluble. It settles out as a white powder. The barium hydroxide is a trifle weaker as a result, but remains pure.

Barium compounds are very poisonous (*barium carbonate*, for instance, is often used as a rat poison), yet a certain barium compound is sometimes taken internally, in large quantities, under a doctor's orders. This may sound queer, but there is a very good reason for it.

The chemical name of barite is *barium sulfate*. (Its

molecule contains an atom of barium, one of sulfur, and four of oxygen.) Barium sulfate is very insoluble, even less soluble than calcium carbonate. Barium compounds can't hurt you unless they go into solution, for only dissolved substances can be absorbed into the body from the intestines. As long as barium sulfate is insoluble, it just passes through the intestines and out without having done you any harm.

Still, why should doctors want you to swallow it? The answer is really simple. X-rays penetrate the simpler atoms, the ones with low numbers, but are stopped by atoms with higher numbers. The bones of the body are made up mostly of calcium (element No. 20) and phosphorus (No. 15). The soft tissues of the body are made up mostly of hydrogen (No. 1), carbon (No. 6), nitrogen (No. 7), and oxygen (No. 8). X-rays therefore pass through skin, flesh, and blood much more easily than they do through bones and teeth. Bones and teeth stand out white against black on the X-ray plate. A doctor can tell where and how a bone may be broken or chipped. A dentist can tell whether there are hidden cavities in teeth.

But sometimes doctors want to know about the intestines of a patient. X-rays give no information under ordinary conditions, and it is a pity to cut the patient open just to look and see. So they feed the patient a "barium meal," a mixture of barium sulfate with malted milk or something like that (to make the barium sulfate a little tastier). Once this is done, the barium sulfate travels slowly along the length of the stomach and intestines and fills them with an element whose number is 56. The barium sulfate stops the X-rays even better than bone does, and it makes a sharp white outline on the X-ray plate. From the shape of the outline, the rate at which it travels, and so on, doctors often get considerable help in making a diagnosis.

GEMS AND POISON

There is a gem stone called *beryl*, which has been known for a long time. The usual variety, opaque and blue or green, is ranked as semi-precious. Transparent varieties are precious. The *aquamarine* is a transparent blue variety; the *emerald*, a transparent green variety. (The emerald is considered the most valuable of all gems.)

In 1798, a Frenchman named L. N. Vauquelin isolated from beryl a compound that he called *glucina* from a Greek word meaning "sweet." (He called it this because some of the compounds he made, using glucina, tasted sweet.) In 1828, two chemists, Friedrich Wöhler and M. Bussy, each isolated the new element that occurs in beryl and in glucina. This element is usually called *beryllium* after beryl, which is now known to be a *beryllium aluminum silicate*. Once in a long while the element may be referred to as *glucinum* after glucina, which is now known to be *beryllium oxide*.

Beryllium is element No. 4. Like magnesium and aluminum, it is protected by a thin layer of the oxide after exposure to air. It is the least active of the alkaline earth metals and by far the hardest. In fact, it resembles aluminum in some ways, more than it resembles the other elements of its own group. It sometimes happens that the first member of a group will resemble the element diagonally to the right and below it in the periodic table. This is an example. Another is oxygen, which in some ways resembles chlorine more than it does sulfur.

Beryllium is very easily penetrated by x-rays because it is so low in atomic number. It can therefore be used as a "window" on x-ray tubes. The x-rays pass through the little beryllium section and come out as a directed beam.

About ten years ago it looked as if beryllium would really come into widespread use in homes and offices, but it turned out otherwise. This is the story.

Cylindrical glass tubes containing a bit of mercury give off light rays and other rays when an electric current travels through. Some of these rays are the invisible but very energetic kind called *ultraviolet rays*. Certain minerals absorb ultraviolet rays and give the energy back in the form of light of various colors. Sometimes the effects are quite beautiful. This ability to shine upon being exposed to invisible ultraviolet rays is called *fluorescence*.

Now an ordinary mercury tube is not very comfortable to read or live by because the color of the light is an eerie and unpleasant green. If the inner surface of the tube is coated with a powder containing a beryllium compound, that powder fluoresces under the mercury's ultraviolet rays and produces a bright, white light. The result was the *fluorescent lights* that became common in kitchens, factories, and offices. These lights were more efficient than ordinary incandescent bulbs. They gave a brighter light with less heat and used up less electric current.

Then came trouble. People who cut themselves on broken fluorescent tubes got wounds that would not heal, and people who breathed the powder from broken fluorescent tubes got very serious lung ailments that couldn't be cured. The beryllium powder used in the fluorescent tubes turned out to be a very sneaky poison that sometimes didn't make itself felt for years. Yet it was a very deadly poison in the long run.

There was only one thing to do, and that was to get along with as little of the poisonous beryllium as possible. The fluorescent tubes manufactured nowadays use newly developed types of powder with little or no beryllium in them.

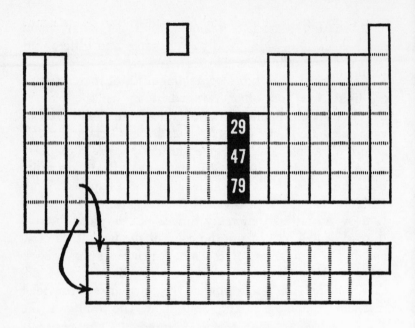

CHAPTER 15

Copper, Silver, and Gold

THE MONEY ELEMENTS

THE FIRST METALS

For hundreds of thousands of years, primitive man used tools made of wood, bone, and stone. Such materials were handy. Metals of various kinds would have been much more useful in many ways, but metals were not handy. Metals usually occur in compounds. To separate the atoms of a metal from the other atoms in a compound is not as

184

easy as picking up a rock and chipping it into an ax head.

It wasn't till six thousand years ago that metals were discovered. Even then the discovery was probably an accident.

The more active a metal is, the more likely it is to occur only in the form of compounds. The more active it is, the harder it is to get it out of the compound. An inert metal, on the other hand, may occur in the soil in free form—that is, as the metal, the element, itself. If an inert metal does occur in a compound, its atoms are usually rather easy to separate.

There are three fairly inert metals that are similar to one another chemically. These are *copper* (element No. 29), *silver* (No. 47), and *gold* (No. 79). Copper derives its name from the Mediterranean island of Cyprus, where there were copper mines in Greek and Roman times. "Silver" and "gold," like "iron," are Anglo-Saxon names.

Silver, being more inert than copper, is more likely to occur free, but it is also less common than copper. Gold is the most inert and also the rarest of the three. Sometimes gold and silver are found mixed as a natural alloy. This mixture is called *electrum*.

We do not know which of the three was discovered first. Samples of all three have been found in Egyptian and Babylonia remains dating back at least to 4000 B.C.

What may have happened is that occasionally someone built a fire on some rock that happened to contain copper, silver, or gold, either free or in the form of a compound. (Copper was the one most likely to be in the form of a compound.) When the fire died down, the man, if he happened to poke through the ashes, may have noticed little metal globules that had been melted out of the rock by the fire. (If the metal was copper in the form of a compound, the burning carbon of the wood fire could easily combine with the other elements of the compound and leave copper behind. You may remember—see page 138— that burning carbon does just this to iron compounds.)

Our primitive man could easily have been attracted by the color and luster of the metal. All three metals are quite beautiful. Copper is reddish-brown, and gold is yellow (they are the only colored metals); silver is white. If the man was curious enough to pound the metal with a rock, he was probably surprised to find that it did not shatter like rock, or splinter like wood or bone. Instead, it bent and flattened out. It could be beaten into any shape.

Undoubtedly, the first use for these shiny little nuggets was as decorations. Since mankind (and womankind, especially) values decorations, there probably began a deliberate search for more metals of all kinds. (Some people, by the way, think the first discovery of metal was made in the Sinai Peninsula, where Africa and Asia meet.)

As centuries passed, man found out that he could make copper harder by adding certain other metals to it. How he discovered this we don't know. Probably it was by accident. In some way he learned to add a little zinc to copper to make *brass*, which is yellower, harder, and cheaper than copper, and to add a little tin to copper to make *bronze*.

The earliest samples of bronze in Egyptian tombs date back to 3500 B.C. For two thousand years and more, bronze was the strong metal. It was used for armor and spearheads, for knives and axes. It was much superior to stone in toughness and in its capacity to keep a sharp edge. It wasn't till iron appeared that something better than bronze was found. Brass was first developed only in the time of the Roman Empire.

A modern copper alloy contains 2 percent beryllium. It

is harder than any copper alloy known to the ancients and is almost as hard as steel (though nowhere nearly as cheap). A piece of beryllium-copper can be bent back and forth without breaking thousands of times more than the best steel. Furthermore, since beryllium-copper doesn't spark when brushed against something hard, tools made of it are particularly useful where inflammable vapors may be in the air.

Copper, silver, and gold were so valuable to people as decorations, and as something to make useful tools out of, that a small quantity of any of the three was worth a great many cows or bushels of grain or heaps of wood. It became handy to have these metals in one's possession because they represented a great value in a small space. A piece of gold worth ten cattle took up far less space than ten cattle and, besides, didn't have to be fed and taken care of. Then, if you wanted cattle to eat, you had only to make the exchange. Man's search for gold has produced about 50,000 tons of it altogether. This is not really much, but then gold is the rarest of all elements except for certain very special ones I'll mention in the last chapter.

Copper, silver, and especially gold became *mediums of exchange*. Gold was rare, it was beautiful, it didn't tarnish, it could be used as jewelry while it was being kept. All possessions began to be valued as worth so many ounces of gold. About 600 B.C. a country called Lydia, in Asia Minor, started using lumps of gold with a government seal and a picture of the king stamped on them. The stamping guaranteed the purity of the gold and its weight. People started demanding such *coins* rather than ordinary lumps of doubtful weight and purity.

Today coins are still made of alloys of copper, silver, and gold. (The pure metals are a little too soft to withstand all the handling coins must get.) Let us look at American coins as examples. The penny is made of a kind of bronze; it is 95 percent copper, 4 percent tin, and 1 percent zinc. The five-cent piece is also mostly copper, though it doesn't look it; it is 75 percent copper and 25 percent nickel. The nickel makes the mixture gray and gives the coin its common name. (There are ancient coins from Bactria, located in the land we now call Afghanistan, which were made up of copper and nickel, too, in just about these proportions.) Silver coins, such as the dime, the quarter, the half-dollar, and the dollar, are 90 percent silver and 10 percent copper. British coins that used to be silver are now made of copper and nickel like the American five-cent piece. Gold coins are 90 percent gold and 10 percent copper. You may never have seen a gold coin because for quite some time now, gold has not been allowed to circulate as coins in the United States. There are complicated economic reasons for this. Now, America's gold supply is simply buried at Fort Knox.

ELECTRICAL WIRING

Copper has a more important use these days than as jewelry or even as coins. Electricity, to be useful, must be led, or conducted, from one place to another. Substances along which electricity can be easily conducted are called *conductors*. Other substances are *non-conductors*. Among the elements, the metals are conductors and the non-metals are non-conductors. (There are some exceptions. Bismuth, although a metal, is a fairly poor conductor. Carbon, although a non-metal, is a fairly good one, at least in the form of graphite.)

When we conduct electricity from place to place, we want to lose as little along the way as possible. The better our conductor, the less electricity we lose. One way of telling how good a conductor we have is to notice how much heat is developed in it as a certain amount of electricity passes through. This heat, which is developed by the *electrical resistance* of the conductor, represents lost electricity. The better the conductor, the lower the resistance and the less the heat and the smaller the loss of electricity.

(Some electrical appliances, of course, are made to turn electricity into heat. They contain special wires that have a great deal of resistance, and those wires get red-hot when a current passes through them. When you use an electric toaster, for example, you want to lose electricity in the form of heat, for it's the heat you want to use.)

Now suppose that you take a number of wires made out of different metals. All the wires are of the same thickness and the same length, and you run the same amount of electricity through each. It turns out that, of all possible wires, silver wires develop the least heat. Silver is therefore the best electrical conductor. Copper is second-best.

If the metals were given marks for their excellence as conductors and silver were given 100, copper would get 95, gold 67, aluminum 58, and iron 16. Since copper is almost as good as silver and is considerably cheaper, it is used for most electrical wiring. Just over half the copper produced is used, in one way or another, in electrical equipment. (As I said on page 132, aluminum is used for long distances to save copper.) Although the alkali metals are the most "metallic metals" as far as their chemical properties are concerned, they are not very good as electrical conductors. Sodium is the best electrical conductor among the alkalis and on the scale above, its rating is only 35.

During World War II, the supply of copper was so desperately short that a large supply of silver was withdrawn from the government vaults at Fort Knox for use as conductors at Oak Ridge. (The silver was returned after the war was over.) In 1943 the government even experimented with copperless pennies, but the experiment was a failure. When new, the 1943 pennies were mistaken for dimes. When old, they turned gray-black and looked ugly. People didn't like them, and in 1944, despite the copper shortage, the government returned to the old copper penny.

Copper (like cobalt; see page 148) is an essential trace element in living tissue. Certain animals, such as crabs, lobsters, snails, and squids, have blue blood, really blue. Their blood contains *hemocyanin,* which carries oxygen the way the red hemoglobin of our blood does. Hemocyanin is a blue compound, and its molecule contains copper atoms.

JEWELRY

Copper is the least inert of the three metals and is therefore least satisfactory as jewelry. When exposed to air, copper first accumulates a brownish coating of oxide as it combines with oxygen; then, more slowly, it turns green as it combines with sulfur compounds in the air and forms a "basic sulfate." Near the sea it forms a "basic chloride" (also green) because of the sodium chloride in the sea spray.

This greenish coating is rather attractive and is valued for that reason. The most spectacular example is the famous Statue of Liberty, in New York harbor, which is made of copper and is now colored bluish-green. The blue-green coating protects the copper underneath from further changes. (Sometimes the green coating is referred to as *verdigris.*)

A common copper ore, *malachite,* has the same attractive color and has been used to make objects of great artistic beauty. This and other copper compounds have supplied artists with blue and green pigments for many centuries.

The color in such copper compounds is not due to copper itself. For instance, *copper sulfate* (with a molecule containing one copper atom, one sulfur atom and four oxygen atoms) is white in color. However, if water is added, each molecule of copper sulfate adds to itself five molecules of water quite loosely held. Such loosely-held water is called *water of hydration* and can easily be driven off by heat. The *hydrated copper sulfate* is a beautiful deep blue in color.

Many salts, like copper sulfate, can be hydrated, with changes in properties. When such water of hydration is removed, the molecules are then said to be *anhydrous.* It often happens that anhydrous salts do not form crystals, whereas the hydrated salts form beautiful crystals. This is certainly the case with copper sulfate. For this reason water of hydration is often called *water of crystallization.*

Copper sulfate, by the way, is used to kill the growth of microscopic plants called algae in water. The inner surface of swimming pools usually appears blue because of a coating of this or of some similar copper compound. It is also used in sprays to kill fungi growing on trees and vines.

Silver is a very beautiful metal out of which to make household objects such as trays, dishes, and cutlery. It has grown less popular now, with modern stainless steel coming into use, but most people still have a set of silver knives, forks, and spoons of various kinds. Objects may be made of solid *sterling silver* (which in this country, is an alloy made up of 90 percent silver and 10 percent copper, while it is 92.5 percent silver and 7.5 percent copper in England) or of *silver plate*. The latter is a cheaper metal, such as iron, covered with a layer of silver put on by electroplating (see page 146).

Silver is easily tarnished by sulfur-containing compounds. In our modern industrial civilization, factories are always discharging smoke that contains a small quantity of sulfur compounds. These react with silver and form a brown black coating of *silver sulfide*. Silver is also easily stained by eggs, which are rich in sulfur compounds.

Gold, as the most inert of the three elements, is the most satisfactory for jewelry. It is not affected by oxygen or by sulfur compounds or by any common acid. Pure gold is too soft for jewelry and would quickly wear away with handling. A certain amount of copper is added to make it harder and more durable.

The purity of gold is measured in *karats*. Completely pure gold is 24-karat gold. British gold coins (92 percent gold) are 22-karat while American gold coins (90 percent gold) are only 21.6-karat. The gold used for jewelry is usually 14-karat gold; that is, it is 14/24 (58 percent) gold and 10/24 (42 percent) copper.

One can make gold jewelry cheaper by piling up the copper in the alloy. After a certain point there is so much copper that exposure to air causes green compounds of copper to form very slowly. That is the reason for the joke about cheap jewelry, given at Christmas, that "turns green in the spring."

Gold is attacked by chlorine. The medieval alchemists knew nothing about chlorine, but when they mixed nitric acid and hydrochloric acid, they found that the mixture would dissolve gold. They called the mixture *aqua regia* (Latin for "royal water") because it dissolved the "king of metals," and the name has stuck with modern chemists. It isn't the acids, though, that dissolve the gold. The two acids, when mixed, react with each other to liberate chlorine. The mixture turns green, and chlorine can actually be smelled in the air above it. It is the chlorine that dissolves the gold.

PHOTOGRAPHY

Since silver is a fairly inert metal, it is easily separated out of its compounds. A common silver compound is *silver chloride*, a white substance with a molecule containing one atom each of silver and chlorine. If silver chloride is exposed to light, the light energy is enough to break the atoms apart. The chlorine is slowly given off as a gas, and the silver remains behind as a very fine powder. Like most powdered metals, finely powdered silver is black.

There are many chemicals that break up silver chloride and form silver metal. If light is allowed to shine upon the silver chloride first, it makes it easier for the silver-producing chemicals to work. This is true even if so little light is used that none of the silver chloride is broken down by the light itself. The light, somehow, simply gets the silver chloride ready to be broken down.

Now suppose that silver chloride (or some similar silver compound) is smeared over a piece of paper, which is then placed in a dark box. Light, reflected from an object and allowed to enter the dark box either through a pinhole or through a focusing lens, forms an image of the object on the sheet of paper. The light is allowed to fall upon the paper for just a short time, and then the paper is removed (in the dark) and treated with a chemical (called a *developer*) to break down the silver chloride. Only those parts of the silver chloride that were struck by the reflected light break down. These parts turn black as powdered silver is formed. The other parts are not affected and show the white of the paper.

In this way, portions of the image that are white and reflect considerable light are reproduced as black on the paper. Portions of the image that are black or deeply colored do not reflect as much light and are reproduced as white. A person with a white face, red lips, and black hair appears on the paper to be a person with a black face, white lips, and white hair. We have produced a *photographic negative*.

If the negative were prepared on something transparent, like glass, light could be shone through it upon a piece of paper coated with silver chloride. The process would be reversed. Light would shine through the unaffected lips and hair of the negative so that they would show up black on the paper. Light would be stopped by the black face so that it would show up white on the paper. A *photographic positive*, or simply a *photograph*, has been produced.

If these negatives or positives were exposed to light, the portions that hadn't blackened would start to blacken as more light hit them. Before they are exposed to light, therefore, they must be treated with a chemical (called a *fixer*) that dissolves away all the silver chloride that is left and leaves behind only the black cloud of powdered silver. The chemical used for the purpose is *sodium thiosulfate* (its molecule containing two atoms of sodium, two of sulfur, and three of oxygen) or, as it is more commonly called, *hypo*.

An earlier photographic process was first worked up in 1837 by a Frenchman named L. J. M. Daguerre, and very early photographs were called daguerreotypes. Since then, there have been tremendous advances in photography. Silver compounds have been prepared in such a sensitive form that exposures to light for only fractions of a second are sufficient. (In older days people had to "pose"; nowadays "action shots" are possible.) A substance called *nitrocellulose,* made out of wood treated with nitric acid, is flexible and transparent, can be prepared in long rolls, and is used for both negatives and positives. An American named George Eastman first prepared such *film* in 1884. Since thousands of negatives could be made on one length of film, motion pictures became possible. Beginning in 1909, *cellulose acetate* (also made out of wood) gradually replaced nitrocellulose. Cellulose acetate is less inflammable and therefore less dangerous. About one-seventh of all the silver produced is now used in photography.

The silver compound, *silver iodide* (its molecule contains one atom of silver and one of iodine), has an interesting modern use. In fine powdered form, it can be sprinkled into clouds from an airplane. Each particle acts as a center about which a raindrop can form. In this way, the cloud is "seeded" and a rainstorm may be started. Scientific "rainmakers" are a possible answer to drought.

THE USELESS METAL

Copper and silver are attractive and precious, and both are useful, too. It is hard to think of electricity without copper wires and even harder to think of photography without silver.

But of what earthly use is gold? Scarcely any. It is all right for jewelry. It can be used for filling teeth. Tiny particles of gold, added to molten glass, will make the glass bright-red or purple. This *ruby-glass* can be used for stained-glass windows. (Copper can be made to do the same thing, while copper oxide will turn glass blue or green.)

Gold is the most malleable of all metals; that is, it can be beaten into the thinnest sheets. (Silver is second.) *Gold leaf* can be made only four-millionths of an inch thick. This was once generally used for the lettering on book covers and is still used for the lettering on doors of offices. Such letters are attractive and don't tarnish or fade with time, and the leaf is so thin that it is not very expensive.

These are about all the uses of gold. As mentioned earlier, it is not even used in coins any more in this country.

One interesting fact about gold is its heaviness. It is one of the heaviest substances known. It is almost three times as heavy as steel. A cubic inch of iron or steel weighs 4½ ounces. A cubic inch of copper weighs 5 ounces, and a cubic inch of silver weighs 6¼ ounces. A cubic inch of gold, however, weighs 11 ounces!

There is an old joke about country boys coming to the city and being sold "gold bricks" by city sharpers, these bricks being ordinary ones covered with gold paint. Actually, one would have to know nothing at all about gold to be fooled. You yourself are already too smart for the sharper, since you know how heavy gold is.

Suppose you had an object as big as an ordinary brick, two by four by eight inches. It would contain 2x4x8, or 64, cubic inches. Such a brick would weigh six pounds or less. A brick of solid gold, however, would weigh no less than forty-four pounds. So, any time a sharper holds out a "gold brick" with one hand, you know it isn't gold without even looking at it. (Such a gold brick, if it were really gold, would be worth $20,000 these days.)

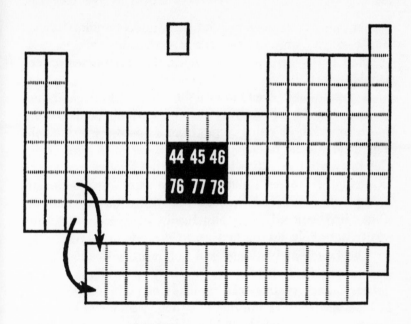

CHAPTER 16 **Platinum**

THE NOBLE ELEMENT

THE USEFULNESS OF NOBILITY

Back on page 54 I said that the inert gases (that is, helium and its relatives) are sometimes called the "noble gases" because they form no compounds and some people seem to think there is something aristocratic about their touch-me-not attitude.

No other elements are completely "noble." All other

197

elements form compounds. But some metals—gold, for instance—do so only with difficulty. Because gold is not affected by oxygen, sulfur, or acids, it is sometimes called a *noble metal*.

A metal that is even more "noble" than gold is *platinum*, element No. 78. This silvery metal was discovered first in South America; its name comes from a Spanish word meaning "little silver," referring to its appearance. It was probably known to the natives long before, but the first European to mention it was an Italian physician named Julius Caesar Scaliger in 1557. The Spanish scientist, Don Antonio de Ulloa, first studied it systematically in 1748, though it wasn't definitely established as an element till 1774.

The fact that platinum will not react with most compounds makes it useful in chemistry laboratories. Little vessels called crucibles can be made of platinum. When it is necessary to heat substances strongly, they can often be heated in these crucibles without fear that they will affect the platinum or be affected by it. Since platinum melts at a temperature of 1,774 degrees centigrade, it can be heated almost to white heat without harm.

When electricity travels through water containing dissolved chemicals, chemical changes usually take place. These changes often take place at the *electrodes*—that is, at the pieces of metal that are introduced into the solution as conductors of the electric current. If the chemical changes taking place are likely to affect ordinary electrodes, platinum electrodes are used instead.

Platinum isn't even affected by fluorine unless the platinum is red-hot, and even then the reaction is a slow one. Fluorine was first isolated, in fact, with equipment made out of platinum.

Platinum isn't completely "noble," of course. Aqua regia

(see page 192) will dissolve it. Strong bases affect it. Certain metals will mix with it. A chemist who is using platinum equipment must always remember the few things that will attack platinum. He must be careful not to expose platinum to these substances, for platinum is at least as expensive as gold, and it would be a shame to spoil any of it. To melt alkaline substances, for instance, platinum crucibles must not be used. Silver crucibles, even iron crucibles, may be used instead.

The rarity and inertness of platinum make it suitable for jewelry, and it is often used as a setting for diamonds. Platinum is one of the metals that we mix with gold when we want to get rid of the yellow color of the gold. The commonest type of such *white gold* is about 10 percent nickel and has a little bit of another metal called zinc. A more expensive variety, also called *platinum gold*, is made of three parts of gold and two parts of platinum. White gold is often used in jewelry.

When platinum was first found in Russia, it was used by counterfeiters who plated it with gold and passed the result as gold coins. Then, in the 1830s and 1840s, Russia issued legal platinum coins. As the price of platinum rose, both coinage and counterfeiting stopped.

THE SEXTUPLETS

Other metals, somewhat resembling platinum, are usually found along with platinum in its ores. There are five of these besides platinum, and the six together are called the *platinum metals*. These six are divided into two groups of three, called *triads*. Each group of three has consecutive element numbers.

The first triad consists of *ruthenium*, No. 44; *rhodium*,

No. 45; and *palladium*, No. 46. The second triad consists of *osmium*, No. 76; *iridium*, No. 77; and, of course, platinum, which is No. 78. All but palladium are more expensive than gold.

If you look at the periodic table, at the beginning or end of the book, you will see that these two triads of elements occur just beneath a triad I have already discussed—iron, cobalt, and nickel, Nos. 26, 27, and 28. The platinum metals are not very similar to iron, cobalt, and nickel, and yet they are not altogether strangers to them, either. The platinum elements are found in small amounts in Canadian nickel mines.

For nearly seventy years after platinum was discovered, it was the only platinum metal known. Then, in the years 1803-1805, four of platinum's five relatives were isolated. An Englishman named W. H. Wollaston discovered palladium and rhodium. Rhodium he named from the Greek word for "rose-red" because some of its compounds had that color. He named palladium after the little planetoid Pallas, which had been discovered in the skies just a few months before. At the same time, an Englishman named Smithson Tennant was studying what was left over when crude platinum was dissolved in aqua regia. In the undissolved left-over he discovered osmium and iridium. He named osmium from a Greek word meaning "smell" because its compound with oxygen, *osmium tetroxide*, had a particularly sharp and irritating odor. (Osmium tetroxide is also very poisonous. Its molecule consists of one atom of osmium and four of oxygen.) He named iridium after the Latin word for "rainbow" because it formed compounds of many colors—green, red, and violet mostly.

Ruthenium, since it is present in crude platinum only in small quantities, escaped notice for a while. It is the rarest of the platinum metals and was finally discovered in 1844 by a chemist named C. E. Claus, who was working with platinum ore from the Ural Mountains in Russia. He named it after Ruthenia, an old name for Russia.

THE NOBLEST AND THE HEAVIEST

Since osmium and iridium were discovered in what was left over when platinum was dissolved in aqua regia, it is obvious that those two metals are not affected by this strong chemical. They are even "nobler" than platinum. Rhodium and ruthenium are also "nobler" than platinum in some ways. Rhodium crucibles may be used at temperatures higher than those at which platinum would begin to soften. Palladium, however, will dissolve in aqua regia, like platinum. Of all the metals, iridium is probably the "noblest."

Silver is sometimes plated with rhodium or palladium to form mirrors or searchlight reflectors. When this is done, sulfur-containing compounds will have no tarnishing effect, and the polished surface will remain shiny permanently.

Osmium and iridium are harder than platinum. Pure platinum, in fact, is too soft for use in laboratory ware. A little iridium (10 percent) is alloyed with it to make it hard enough for use.

This same platinum-iridium alloy is used for *standard measures*. (These are basic measurements with which all similar measures must be compared.) There is, for instance, in a safe place in a Paris suburb, a platinum-iridium bar with two marks on it. The distance between the marks at a temperature of zero degrees centigrade is called a *meter*. This is the *International Standard Meter*. Most of the countries of the world have agreed to define their measures of length according to that meter. A *yard*, for instance, is exactly 3,600/3,937 meter.

There is also a lump of platinum-iridium alloy, the weight of which is called a *kilogram*. This is the standard measure of weight. (A kilogram is about two and a fifth pounds.)

Osmium and iridium form an alloy called *osmiridium*. This alloy occurs naturally and usually contains some of the other platinum metals, too. Osmiridium is very hard and is sometimes used for the tips of fountain-pen points and for phonograph needles.

The platinum metals are rather poor conductors of electricity. They are only a sixth as good as copper or silver. This property is sometimes useful. A poor conductor of electricity, as we saw on page 189, heats up when electricity travels through it. If the wire is thin enough, the heat can make it glow white-hot. For this reason, osmium was once used as the filament in electric-light bulbs. Osmium has the highest melting point of all the platinum metals (2,750 degrees centigrade), and white heat doesn't melt it.

The platinum metals are heavy. Ruthenium, rhodium, and palladium are heavier than silver. Osmium, iridium, and platinum are heavier than gold and are, in fact, the heaviest substances that exist on earth.

Platinum is 10 percent heavier than gold. That 44-pound gold brick I mentioned on page 196 would weigh 49 pounds if it were made of platinum. Iridium and osmium are heavier still. A brick made of either would weigh 51 pounds. (Osmium is just a trifle heavier than iridium and is the heaviest substance known.)

THE BLACK POWDER SPEED-UP

In the presence of platinum, hydrogen will combine with oxygen at room temperature and will attach itself to many organic molecules. In the presence of platinum, oxygen will combine with sulfur dioxide to form sulfur trioxide —one of the steps in the formation of the very useful sulfuric acid. In all these ways, platinum behaves as a catalyst.

If platinum is broken up into tiny pieces, it works more efficiently. When so ground up, it appears black, as most powdered metals do. It is then called *platinum black*. In order to make it easy to handle small quantities of this valuable material, we deposit it on an inert substance such as asbestos. *Platinized asbestos* is the catalyst actually used in many industrial processes. Chemical reactions that would take almost forever without it proceed quickly when it is used. It is a speed-up device that can make all the difference between something that is only theoretically possible and something that is practical.

The only trouble is the expense. Because platinum is very expensive, other chemical substances that work somewhat like platinum are used instead. Usually they are nowhere nearly as good, but their cheapness makes up for the lack of efficiency.

Palladium is also a good catalyst for hydrogen reactions. An interesting thing about palladium is the way it absorbs hydrogen. A piece of palladium will absorb five hundred times its own volume of hydrogen at ordinary temperatures (and will grow a bit bulkier as it does so). It absorbs even more hydrogen at higher temperatures. Hydrogen will pass right through a sheet of palladium by combining with it on one side and coming loose again on the other side.

The other platinum metals also absorb hydrogen, but not nearly so well as palladium.

Palladium is also used in jewelry as platinum is. It can be used to form still another variety of white gold (see page 199). Nine parts of gold mixed with one part of palladium form an alloy known as *palladium gold*, which is white.

Platinum expands as the temperature goes up and contracts as it goes down, just as most substances do. The amount of its expansion and contraction is just about the same as that of ordinary glass. This means that, if molten glass is solidified round a platinum wire, the two substances will expand and contract together as the temperature changes. Most other metals expand or contract more than glass or less than glass. If glass were solidified round wires of such metals, there would be a certain amount of pulling, where metal met glass, every time the temperature changed, and eventually something would break. For this reason, the wires inside electric-light bulbs used to be connected to the outside by little pieces of platinum wire sticking through the glass. Nowadays we have special alloys, made of cheap metals, that expand and contract just as glass does, and wires of these alloys are now used instead of wires of platinum. One of these is a nickel-iron alloy called *platinite*.

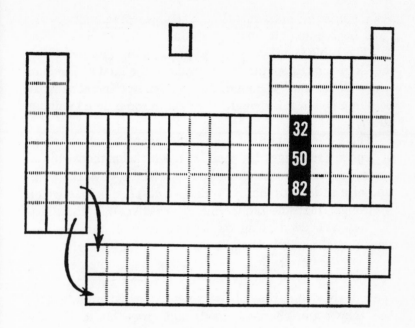

CHAPTER 17 **Tin and Lead**

THE CANNER'S AND PAINTER'S ELEMENTS

THE GARDEN OF EDEN AND THE TIN ISLES

Carbon and silicon are both non-metals, but under them in the periodic table are three metals. Two of these metals should be quite familiar to all of us, for they have been known since ancient times. They are *tin*, element No. 50, and *lead*, element No. 82. Both names are Anglo-Saxon, like those of iron, silver, and gold.

Samples of both metals (or alloys containing them) have been found in remains dating as far back as 3,000 B.C. The Bible mentions lead and perhaps tin. (In describing the Garden of Eden, the Bible speaks of the land of Havilah, where "bdellium" is found. No one knows for sure what bdellium is, but it is thought to be tin or some tin-containing alloy.)

The earliest important use of tin was in the manufacture of bronze (see pages 136 and 186), which for thousands of years was the hardest metal known. (These days the addition of a little phosphorus produces *phosphor bronze* which is stronger than the bronze the ancients knew.) The Phoenicians, who lived along the eastern coast of the Mediterranean Sea, navigated long distances to the mysterious Tin Isles of the far-off Atlantic, bringing back tin ore. They guarded the secret location of the Tin Isles very carefully, since, if they were the only ones who knew where to get tin ore, they could charge a good, high price for it. We are pretty certain, though, that the Tin Isles were actually the Cornish districts at the southwestern tip of Great Britain, together with some small islands off that coast.

Tin is still obtainable there in the form of *stannic oxide*, whose molecule contains one atom of tin and two of oxygen. (The word "stannic" comes from the Latin name for tin, which was "stannum.") The stannic oxide ore is called *cassiterite* or *tinstone*. Such stannic oxide (purified, of course, for the ore found in nature is impure) is added to glazes to turn them into white enamel. Since it makes a transparent substance opaque, it is called an *opacifier*.

The English mines are pretty well played out today. Tin (which is really a rather rare metal) is now obtained mostly from the Malay Peninsula in southeastern Asia and to some extent from Bolivia in South America. During World War

II, when Japan occupied the Malay Peninsula, the United States was pretty hard put to it to conserve what tin it had. People had to turn in old toothpaste tubes when they bought new ones, because the tubes contained tin.

Tin is still used in making bronze, but that is no longer its main use. (In fact, the expensive tin in bronze is being replaced by the cheaper aluminum more and more. Such *aluminum bronze* is quite satisfactory for almost all purposes.) Tin can take a high polish, and it isn't affected by oxygen, water, or weak acids. It can therefore be used in contact with foods (which are often weakly acid) without being tarnished or corroded and without affecting the food. For that reason, the steel cans that are used to preserve food are lined with tin. That is why they are usually referred to as "tin cans." The British call them simply "tins." The names are, of course, not quite right. Pure tin is too expensive (it is three times as expensive as copper) and too weak to be made into cans; it is used only as a lining. Such tin-coated iron is usually called *tin-plate.* Half the tin produced these days is used in cans.

Tin is not ductile enough to be made into wires. It is quite malleable, however, and can be beaten into thin sheets called *tin foil.* Because of tin's inertness, tin foil was used to wrap food such as candy. These days, because tin is expensive, tin foil has been replaced by aluminum foil, but such is the force of habit that many people still call it "tin foil." In every possible way, in fact, industry is making do with less tin wherever possible, especially since the World War II emergency taught them to use substitutes.

In one way tin betrays its relationship to carbon and silicon. At temperatures lower than 18 degrees centigrade (this is 65 degrees Fahrenheit), ordinary metallic tin, called *white tin,* changes into an allotropic form called

gray tin. Gray tin is not really a metal at all, but a non-
metal with certain resemblances to carbon and silicon.
Gray tin crumbles away into a powder. The change isn't
very rapid unless the temperature drops well below freezing.
In a cold city like Leningrad, tin objects have been known
to crumble away. People who first observed this crumbling
called it "tin rot," "tin plague," "tin pest" or "tin disease."
Not one of these names is really suitable.

There is another dramatic phrase in connection with
tin. The metal is made up of small crystals and when a strip
of tin is bent, the crystals slide against one another, making
a creaking noise. This is called "the cry of tin."

PLUMBERS AND PAINTERS

The ancient Romans used lead for cisterns to store drinking
water, pipes to conduct the drinking water, and drains to
lead waste water away. It is for this reason that people who
work on water pipes and such objects are called "plumbers"
(from the Latin word for lead, which is "plumbum"). You
see how habits hang on. They're still called plumbers even
though water pipes aren't made of lead any more.

Lead has some good points as water pipe. It is soft and
easy to roll into pipe even without modern machinery, for
one thing. (In fact, it is the softest of the common metals
and can be scratched with the fingernail. Before the days
of graphite, sticks of soft lead were used to make marks.
That is why graphite pencils are still called "lead pencils,"
why thin sticks of graphite for mechanical pencils are called
"leads" and why an old-fashioned name for graphite is
"plumbago" which, as you see, is from the Latin word for
"lead.")

Another advantage lead has is that it isn't affected by water that is slightly alkaline (as natural water often is), and it lasts a long time. Some of the old Roman pipes are still being used today. If a few hundredths of a percent of tellurium is added to lead, the alloy is particularly resistant to corrosion. But lead has one terribly bad point. Water that is slightly acid corrodes the lead and dissolves some lead compounds. These are poisonous. An ounce of a lead compound is enough to poison 25,000 gallons of water.

Lead collects in the bones and stays there. The body can't get rid of it except very slowly. For this reason, even if the lead compounds in the water at any one time are not enough to be poisonous, they can build up over a long time and do harm. In other words, lead poisoning is cumulative. It is for this reason that water pipes are now made of iron, brass, or copper.

The most important modern use of lead is as a coloring matter in paint—that is, as a *pigment*. One lead compound used in this way is *basic lead carbonate,* commonly called *white lead.* It has a rather complicated molecule containing three atoms of lead, two of carbon, two of hydrogen, and eight of oxygen. It is mixed with linseed oil to form a white paint that will stay bright and white for a long time if exposed only to fairly pure air, water, and ordinary weather. In our modern industrial civilization, however, the air often contains sulfur compounds that result from burning coal. These compounds attack white lead and form *lead sulfide* (the molecule containing one atom of lead and one of sulfur). Since lead sulfide is black, white-lead paint gradually darkens.

(Lead sulfide, by the way, occurs in the soil, and is then called *galena.* This is the most important lead ore.

Lead is rare, as tin is, but since lead ores are scattered all over the world, lead is far less expensive than tin.)

Blackening by sulfur is just one of the troubles with lead paint. There is also the problem of poison. Painters used to pick up lead poisoning so often from handling lead-containing paints that the sickness is commonly called *painter's colic*.

There are other pigments that contain lead. One such is *red oxide of lead*, or, as it is oftener called, *red lead*. (Sometimes it is called *minium*.) Its molecule contains three atoms of lead and four of oxygen, and it has a brick-red color. Red lead is used in *primers*—that is, in paints used as the first coat over steel. The brick-red color of steel girders being used in construction is due to red lead.

Another important lead compound is *tetraethyl lead*. Here a lead atom is combined with four hydrocarbon groups (see page 70). Tetraethyl lead is added to gasoline to reduce "knocking" (that is, premature explosions of gasoline in the cylinders) and increase power. Gasoline so treated is called *Ethyl gas*.

If tetraethyl lead were the only substance added to gasoline, a lead "ash" might be left behind on cylinders and pistons, ruining the engine. To prevent this, an organic compound containing bromine is also added to the gasoline. As the gasoline burns, the lead and bromine combine to form *lead bromide* (whose molecule contains one atom of lead and two of bromine). Lead bromide doesn't boil below 900 degrees centigrade, but this temperature is reached in the automobile engine. Lead bromide vaporizes and is blown out in the exhaust, and the lead atoms, having done their work, are gotten rid of.

Lead has still another use in the automobile of today. The *storage battery* that supplies electricity for the self-starter, the lights, the radio, and so on consists of alternate plates of lead and *lead dioxide* (the molecule containing one atom of lead and two of oxygen). These plates are surrounded by strong sulfuric acid. As the storage battery works, the lead and lead dioxide both combine with the sulfuric acid to form *lead sulfate* (the molecule containing one atom of lead, one of sulfur, and four of oxygen). When the battery is recharged, the lead sulfate is changed back to lead and lead dioxide. The lead used for battery plates contains 9 percent antimony. These days such plates represent the largest single use for both lead and antimony.

There is a kind of glass that is made almost entirely of *lead silicate*. This *flint glass*, since it bends light (see page 68) more than ordinary glass, can be cut into facets with a gem-like effect. It is therefore used for making the imitation gems called paste. It is also very clear and transparent and is therefore used for lenses in optical instruments such as microscopes as well as in eyeglasses. Such glass is formed by heating *lead monoxide* (also called *litharge*, its molecule containing one atom of lead and one of oxygen) with sand and potassium carbonate.

Most lead compounds are not particularly soluble in water. An exception is *lead acetate*, which is commonly called *sugar of lead*. The name comes from the fact that the compound tastes sweet, but don't let that fool you. Sweet it may taste, but it is very poisonous for all that.

WEIGHT AND MELTING POINT

As a metal, lead isn't very impressive. It is rather gray, and it doesn't take a polish. It is soft and weak. People thought of it as a cheap and rather worthless metal. In Shakespeare's *The Merchant of Venice* the heroine, Portia, had her suitors choose among three closed caskets. If one of them chose the casket containing her portrait, she would marry him. One of the caskets was gold and one silver. These were symbols of wealth. The third, which actually contained her portrait, was of lead, a symbol of poverty. (The hero was supposed to disregard external show, you see, for the true worth within.)

The one thing about lead that impressed people was its weight. It is over 50 percent heavier than iron and even a trifle heavier than silver. (It is only half as heavy as gold or platinum, but few people, especially in earlier times, handled those precious metals.) Since lead was the heaviest common metal, it was used where weight was important. It made good shot and bullets, for instance, since a heavy bullet does more damage than a light one of the same size. A little bit of arsenic added to the lead makes it harder and more useful for this purpose.

Tin also, although it is quite expensive, somehow has the reputation of being cheap and inferior. In the early days of automobile manufacture, lower-priced cars were sometimes jokingly referred to as "tin lizzies."

A useful characteristic of lead is that it melts at 328 degrees centigrade, which is low for a metal. Tin melts at an even lower temperature, 232 degrees centigrade. The two together form alloys that melt lower still and are useful for that reason.

I've already talked about fusible alloys and type metal (see page 120). They contain antimony or bismuth, but they also contain tin or lead or both. Wood's metal, for instance, is 50 percent bismuth, but it also contains 25 percent lead and 12½ percent tin. Type metal is 5 percent antimony, 3 percent tin, and 82 percent lead. *Pewter*, which was once used to make cheap dishes (at a time when expensive ones were made out of silver or silverplate), is mostly tin.

Tin and lead, alloyed in various proportions, form *solder*. Solder is low-melting and soft. When a thick wire of it is pressed against a lump of metal that has been heated in a fire or by means of an electric current (a *soldering iron*), the solder melts easily. The liquid solder is allowed to drip over two pieces of metal (iron, perhaps, or copper) that are held near one another. As the solder freezes again, it hangs on firmly to both pieces of metal. In this way, the two pieces become one piece, and solder acts as a kind of metallic glue. It would be difficult to set up electric circuits if wires couldn't be soldered together quickly and easily.

CHEMICAL PREDICTION

The element that lies between silicon and tin in the periodic table is *germanium,* element No. 32. It was discovered in 1886 by a German chemist named C. A. Winkler, who named it after Germany.

The most dramatic thing about germanium is the mere fact that it was discovered. In 1869 a Russian chemist, D. I. Mendeleev, worked out the periodic table and showed that elements in the same column had similar properties. In his day, of course, not all the elements were known; so there were "holes" in the periodic table.

In 1871 Mendeleev stated that new elements would be discovered to fill those holes. He picked three elements in particular that would fit three particular holes. One of them was the element that he said belonged under silicon and above tin. He called it *eka-silicon* and predicted what its characteristics would be when it was discovered. ("Eka" is the Sanskrit word for "one" so that "eka-silicon" means the element in "hole number one" under silicon.) He used as his guide the known properties of silicon and tin.

All three of Mendeleev's elements were soon discovered, and his predictions hit the mark in every case. Germanium was the last of the three, and it put the finishing touch on the whole matter. No one has ever questioned the value of the periodic table since.

In recent years, a most unexpected use has been discovered for germanium. A piece of germanium metal containing small quantities of certain impurities, under the proper conditions, will conduct electricity in one direction but not in another. It acts as a *rectifier,* in other words. It also acts as an *amplifier;* that is, it makes small currents into large ones. For this purpose, germanium must be free of certain metals, such as arsenic. One part of arsenic per billion would spoil everything.

The vacuum tubes in radios, television sets, and other electronic equipment serve exactly that purpose. They are rectifiers and amplifiers. This means that a tiny piece of germanium (called a *transistor*) can do the work of a much larger vacuum tube. The transistor takes far less power, develops far less heat, and lasts much longer than vacuum tubes do. Since a great deal of the space in electronic instruments is taken up by vacuum tubes, the use of transistors instead may mean that radios no bigger than a wristwatch (and other such marvels) will become practical in the near future. (Even more recently, pieces of silicon have been made to work as transistors. Germanium and silicon are known as *semi-conductors* because they don't carry electricity as well as most metals, but carry it somewhat better than most non-metals.)

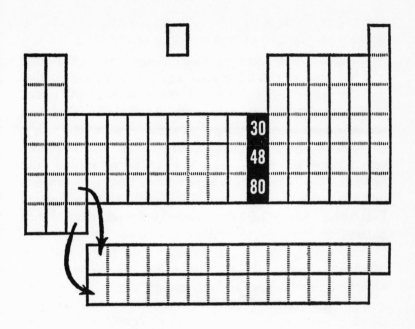

CHAPTER 18   **Mercury**

THE LIQUID ELEMENT

THE DIFFERENT METAL

In the previous chapter, I said that tin and lead melt at temperatures as low as 200 or 300 degrees centigrade. The alkali metals, as we have seen, melt at even lower temperatures, and one of them, cesium, turns liquid on a hot summer day.

There is one metal, however, that is liquid even on a

cold day. That metal is *mercury,* element No. 80. Mercury doesn't solidify, in fact, until a temperature of 39 degrees below zero centigrade is reached. It wasn't until 1759 that it was frozen in the laboratory, and it was only then that chemists were willing to admit that it was a real metal.

The Greeks and Romans called mercury *hydrargyrum,* which means "liquid silver." We ourselves often call it *quicksilver,* "quick" meaning alive. If you have ever played with a bit of mercury (and it is a fascinating substance to fool around with), you may have noticed that small droplets will roll away quickly if any finger pressure is brought to bear upon them. They dart away as though alive; hence *quick*silver.

The name "mercury" is inherited from the chemists of the Middle Ages, who used to name the various metals after heavenly bodies. Gold was named "sun," silver "moon," iron "Mars," copper "Venus," and so on, in their writings, which often contained quite a bit of astrology and other things we don't think much of today. None of these fancy names stuck except the one for the liquid metal, hydrargyrum, which they named "Mercury." We still call it that today.

Mercury is a heavy substance. It is twice as heavy as iron and a third heavier than lead. A lead ball would float in mercury. A pint of mercury weighs fourteen and a half pounds. If you ever come across a bottle of mercury in a chemistry laboratory, try to lift it. At first you will naturally use only as much force as you would for a bottle of some such liquid as water or alcohol. When you do that, the bottle of mercury will feel as though it were nailed to the table. You will have to use a lot more force to lift it, and you will probably be glad to put it down.

As the heaviest known liquid at room temperature,

mercury has an important use in weather prediction. One of the pieces of information that go into weather prediction is the weight of the air above us. As a result of the heat of the sun, combined with the effect of oceans and mountains, the atmosphere piles up in some places to form *high-pressure areas* and thins out in other places to form *low-pressure areas*. These areas travel about the earth. Clear weather is usually associated with high pressures and stormy weather with low pressures.

The differences in pressure aren't great. A high-pressure area may have 10 percent more air above it than a low-pressure area. This isn't enough to affect our breathing or anything else about us. We have to use instruments to measure the changing pressure.

One way to measure the air pressure is to balance a column of liquid against it. The air above a square inch of the earth's surface might weigh as much as a column of water thirty-four feet high above that same square inch. If the air pressure were low, the air might weigh only as much as a column of water thirty-three feet high. If we balanced a column of water against the air (this can be done quite easily), we could follow changes in the air pressure by watching the changes in the height of the water column.

But a water column as tall as a four-story building isn't particularly convenient. We therefore use a column of mercury instead. Since mercury weighs fourteen and a half times as much as water, a column of mercury thirty inches high weighs as much as a column of water (of equal thickness) thirty-four feet high.

A glass tube containing thirty inches of mercury balanced against the air pressure is a *barometer*. The height of that mercury column is measured carefully, and in every weather report you will hear the air pressure given to the nearest hundredth of an inch, as so many inches of mercury. The weather man will also say whether the barometer is steady, rising, or falling. If it is rising, fair weather is usually on the way. If it is falling, stormy weather is coming. If it is steady, the weather will continue as it is.

Another common use of mercury is for the measurement of temperature. Mercury expands as the temperature goes up and contracts as it goes down, as just about all substances do. Mercury does it in a very regular way, expanding evenly over a considerable range of temperature.

Now suppose you had a little container full of mercury with a very thin tube extending out from the container. If the temperature went up, the mercury would expand a bit, and it could do this only by creeping up the tube a bit. If the temperature went down, the mercury would contract and sink down the tube.

A bulb of mercury attached to a thin tube is a *thermometer*. If a thermometer were placed in melting ice, the height to which the mercury rose in the tube could be marked as zero degrees centigrade (or 32 degrees Fahrenheit). If it were placed in boiling water, the height of the mercury column could be marked as 100 degrees centigrade (or 212 degrees Fahrenheit). The space between the marks could then be divided evenly down to single degree marks.

Mercury isn't the only liquid that can be used in thermometers. Ordinary household thermometers, hung outside a window to show the outdoor temperature, usually contain, instead of mercury, a liquid containing a red dye that makes it easy to see.

Mercury doesn't wet glass; that is, a thin layer of mercury doesn't stick to the glass as it moves up and down. (A thin layer of water does.) For this reason, mercury slips up and down a tube very easily. This is important for both barometers and thermometers.

In a thermometer, the mercury is sealed in a vacuum. In a barometer, however, the mercury is in contact with air at one end. It is another good point about mercury, therefore, that it isn't affected by air under ordinary conditions.

Mercury conducts electricity since it is metal. Some is placed in a little horizontal cylinder with electrical contacts at one end. If the cylinder is tilted one way, the mercury touches the contacts and closes the circuits. If it is tilted the other way, the mercury moves away from the contacts and the circuit is broken. Such *mercury switches* are used in industry and even in the home. (Unlike old-fashioned switches, they make no noise as they put the lights on and off.) They represent the most important use of mercury these days.

DENTISTS AND WEDDING RINGS

Like lead compounds, mercury compounds are generally poisonous. Mercury, in fact, has a danger about it that lead does not have. Mercury boils at only 357 degrees centigrade, which is a lower boiling point than any other metal has. Even at lower temperatures, mercury gives off a certain amount of vapor. This vapor is poisonous to breathe and is cumulative in its effects. For this reason, chemists never heat mercury without arranging for a draft of air to carry off the vapor.

Nevertheless, most of us have some mercury in our mouths all the time. You see, mercury mixes with many metals to form alloys called *amalgams*. It does so with silver alloys, for instance, to form *silver amalgam*. When it is first formed, silver amalgam is soft and can be molded like clay. After a few minutes, however, it hardens.

Dentists, once they have drilled out a decayed part of a tooth, make a bit of the silver amalgam (which contains a small amount of tin, copper, and zinc, as well as silver) and squeeze it into the cavity as a "silver filling." Such a filling is scarcely affected by air, saliva, or food. Since the mercury atoms are held very tightly by the silver atoms and don't vaporize or dissolve, they are no danger to us.

Gold amalgam is also used for fillings. Mercury mixes with gold quite easily and quickly, and this is something you must remember if you want to play with a little mercury. Take your rings off! My wife once poured a drop of mercury from hand to hand and ruined her wedding ring completely. The yellow color was gone. It looked quite gray and ordinary. She was quite upset, as you can imagine.

Amalgams are useful to the chemist. Sodium metal, for instance, is used for many purposes but is so reactive that it is a safety problem. It will, however, mix with mercury to form *sodium amalgam.* This will do many of the jobs sodium itself will do and is much safer to handle.

Another well-known use of mercury these days is in special lamps. A droplet of mercury, heated by an electric current, is converted to vapor, which glows with light and gives off the powerful ultraviolet rays. Mercury is used in "sun-lamps" that can tan you in wintertime to a nice Miami brown (or sunburn you, if you're not careful). It is also used in fluorescent lamps, in which the ultraviolet rays set a powder coating within the tube to glowing with a bright white light (see page 183).

Mercurous chloride (its molecule containing two atoms of mercury and two of chlorine) is more commonly known as *calomel.* It has been used in the past as a laxative. It is dangerous, though, and, unless used very carefully, can poison. Its close relative, *mercuric chloride* (its molecule containing only one atom of mercury and two of chlorine), is much more dangerous. Its common name is *corrosive sublimate,* and a little of that will kill you no matter how carefully you take it.

Mercuric oxide is a brick-red compound with a molecule containing one atom of mercury and one of oxygen. It is interesting historically as the compound that Priestley was heating when he discovered oxygen. Another red mercury compound is *mercuric sulfide* (its molecule containing one atom of mercury and one of sulfur). It occurs naturally in the earth and, under the commoner name *cinnabar,* is the most important mercury ore. The pure compound is used as a bright-red pigment and is then called *vermilion.*

Mercury fulminate (its molecule containing one atom each of mercury, oxygen, nitrogen, and carbon) is an extremely touchy explosive. A bit of it will explode violently if it is just struck lightly. (Most useful explosives require a bit more than that to go off—which is fortunate, as otherwise people who have to make or use explosives would be forever blowing themselves to pieces.) A trifling amount of mercury fulminate is used as a *detonator* to set off a larger amount of a less sensitive explosive, such as dynamite. The fulminate may be set off electrically from a distance, and the shock of its explosion will then set off the dynamite.

Finally, *Mercurochrome,* which you may be familiar with as a mild antiseptic to put on minor cuts and scrapes, has a complex molecule containing a mercury atom.

BATTERIES AND PROTECTIVE PLATING

The two metals just above mercury in the periodic table

resemble each other closely. One of them, *zinc*, element No. 30, seems to have been known in ancient times, for alloys containing it have been dated as far back as 1500 B.C. The metal itself, however, wasn't isolated until 1746, when a German chemist named Andreas Sigismund Marggraf turned the trick. The name of the element, from the German, has no other meaning so far as we know.

The oldest use of zinc was in a copper alloy called brass. Zinc added to copper made it tougher, harder, and stronger. When the zinc content was 35 or 40 percent, the brass was hardest. We can make it harder still these days by adding nickel (as much as 12 percent). The resulting alloy is called *nickel brass*.

A common use of brass is for buttons and other ornaments on uniforms and fancy dress. (A mixture of 80 percent copper and 20 percent zinc, sometimes called *Dutch metal*, results in an alloy where the red color of copper has paled to just the color of gold.) The higher the rank of an officer in the armed services, the fancier the uniform and its trimmings. That is how the slang term "top brass" originated.

The addition of nickel to brass masks the copper color altogether so that not much nickel is required to turn the alloy quite white (as in the American nickel, or five-cent piece, which is three-fourths copper but shows no copper color). For that reason, nickel brass is sometimes called *nickel silver* or *German silver*, but these are misleading names for there is no silver in the alloy.

A brass containing 40 percent zinc (*Muntz metal*) resists corrosion. For that reason it can be used for forming protective layers over ship bottoms with more success than copper can.

Nowadays, an important use of zinc is in *dry batteries*, the kind we think of as "flashlight batteries." Such a battery

has an outer shell of zinc (just under the cardboard covering) and a carbon rod in the center. Between the two are
a variety of chemicals.

The zinc, the carbon, and the chemicals in between
react with one another to form electricity. If the battery is
just allowed to stand, the electricity is dammed up and
cannot flow. If the two *terminals* at one end of the battery
(one is connected to the zinc shell, the other to the carbon
rod) are connected by a metal wire, electricity will flow
along the wire. If the electricity is made to run through a
light bulb on the way, the bulb will light up. Naturally,
the electricity will flow only if there is no break in the wire
—that is, if the circuit is closed. An ordinary flashlight will
not light until we push the switch. That closes a break in
the wire and completes the circuit. The bulb then lights.

Zinc is one of several metals that we may use to plate
iron or steel to prevent rusting. We can do this by dipping
a clean iron sheet into molten zinc or by electroplating
(see page 146). An old-fashioned name for electricity is
galvanism, and iron covered by zinc is called *galvanized
iron.* Pails are often made of galvanized iron; when they are
new, you can see the crystal shapes of zinc on the surface.

Zinc compounds have largely taken the place of poisonous beryllium compounds used in fluorescent lights that I
spoke of on page 183.

Zinc is quite an active metal. In classroom chemistry
demonstrations, zinc is often added to acid, and hydrogen
is released as a result. (The zinc atoms replace the hydrogen
atoms in the molecules of acid.) In this way, hydrogen can
be collected and its properties studied. However, it is important to use a good grade of zinc for the purpose. Poor
grades contain small quantities of arsenic. On treatment
with acid, the extremely poisonous arsine, which I men-

tioned in Chapter 9, is released in possibly fatal amounts. It is better to take some pains about this beforehand than to suffer the pains afterward.

Another metal used to plate iron and steel is the one just under zinc in the periodic table. This metal is so similar to zinc that it occurs with zinc in zinc ore. It was discovered in zinc ore by Friedrich Strohmeyer in 1817.

The commonest zinc ore is *zincblende,* which is made up mostly of *zinc sulfide* (with a molecule containing one atom of zinc and one of sulfur). The Greek word for this ore was "kadmeia"; so Strohmeyer called the new metal *cadmium.* It is element No. 48.

Cadmium plating is better than zinc plating, but more expensive. Cadmium takes a higher polish and protects more efficiently against rust. Another kind of protective action of cadmium comes into play when a bit of it is added to silver. It makes silver immune to the tarnishing effect of sulfur compounds. There is also cadmium in Wood's metal (a fusible alloy) and in some solders. Cadmium, you see, is about as low-melting as lead. A bit of cadmium (one percent) added to copper makes for a metal strong enough to use in trolley wires, without cutting down electrical conductivity.

An interesting modern use of cadmium is in connection with nuclear reactors in atomic power stations. Cadmium rods thrust into holes in the reactor slow down the nuclear reaction when such a slowdown is desired. Such rods can prevent a catastrophic explosion. They are operated automatically in such a way that they slide into the holes at the first sign of too much heat.

Zinc oxide, with a molecule containing one atom of zinc and one of oxygen, is an important white pigment, used in paints. It is often called *zinc white.* It doesn't have the *covering power* of white lead; that is, an ounce of zinc white in paint won't cover as large an area of wood thickly enough to hide the wood's natural color as an ounce of white lead will. But zinc white isn't poisonous, and it isn't darkened by sulfur compounds. (Zinc sulfide is formed, but it is white so that it leaves the color of the pigment unchanged. Zinc sulfide itself is cheaper and, mixed with barium sulfate, can also be used as a somewhat inferior white paint. The mixture is called *lithopone*.)

Cadmium sulfide (its molecule contains an atom of cadmium and one of sulfur) is used as a yellow pigment.

Since zinc oxide is used for dental cements, you may have some in your teeth. It is also used in face powder; so, if you are a girl, you may have some on your face, too. Zinc oxide is also the powder you see in *calamine lotion*. (That powder is pink because it also contains about one-half of 1 percent iron oxide.)

Finally, zinc is one of the necessary trace elements in living tissue.

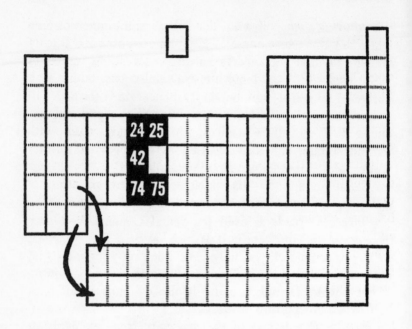

CHAPTER 19 **Chromium**

THE COLOR ELEMENT

PLATE AND PAINT

I have already mentioned several metals—nickel, tin, cadmium and zinc—that can be plated over iron or steel to prevent rusting. The most beautiful type of plating involves another metal, *chromium*, which is element No. 24.

Chromium was discovered by N. L. Vauquelin in 1797, and he named it from the Greek word for "color" because all its compounds are colored. (They also come in almost every possible color.) The metal itself is among the hardest of the elements, being harder than iron, cobalt, or nickel. It doesn't tarnish in air, being protected, like aluminum, by a thin layer of oxide, and it takes a brilliant polish.

The decorative metalwork on automobiles is steel plated first with nickel and then with a thin layer of chromium. Most people refer to this kind of metalwork as "chrome."

Chromium is not only plated over steel. It is also added to steel to form useful alloys. Some *chrome-steels* are particularly hard and strong and are used for the balls in ball-bearings. *Stainless steel* contains 18 percent or less chromium and 8 percent or less nickel. It doesn't rust and is used very commonly these days for cutlery. Stainless steel is not magnetic. If you own a magnet and a knife with a stainless steel blade, you can test that for yourself.

Another interesting chromium alloy you will find in the home is *nichrome*. This alloy contains four parts of nickel to one part of chromium and sometimes some iron. Nichrome, for a metal, is a very poor conductor of electricity, only 1½ percent as good as silver. Electricity led through a nichrome wire quickly heats it to a red heat even if the wire is quite thick. The wire that glows in toasters when you turn on the electricity is often made of nichrome.

Chromic oxide (its molecule contains two atoms of chromium and three of oxygen) is green. It is obtained from an ore called *chromite*, whose molecule is a combination of chromic oxide and iron oxide. Chromite is the commonest chromium ore, and is very high-melting. It is formed into bricks and used to line high-temperature furnaces.

Chromic oxide can be added to glass to give it a green color. The colors of emerald and ruby are due to small quantities of chromic oxide. The different colors (emeralds are green and rubies red) depend on the size of the chromic oxide particles. Sapphires, which are blue, sometimes contain chromic oxide. The aluminum and beryllium compounds that make up the main structure of these gems are colorless.

Chromic oxide, when used in paints, is known as *chrome green*. *Lead chromate*, called *chrome yellow* (its molecule contains one atom of lead, one of chromium, and four of oxygen), and *basic lead chromate*, called *chrome red* (its molecule contains two atoms of lead, one of chromium, and five of oxygen), are used in paints. A mixture of the two, called *chrome orange*, is also used in paints.

THE HARD STEELS

Several elements near chromium in the periodic table share its hardness. They are valuable because, when added to steel, they increase its toughness and hardness.

These metals are *manganese*, element No. 25; *molybdenum*, No. 42; and *wolfram*, No. 74.

The commonest manganese ore is *pyrolusite*, which consists of *manganese dioxide* (whose molecule contains one atom of manganese and two of oxygen.) It is fairly common. In fact, next to iron, manganese is the most common of the heavier metals. It resembles iron (its right hand neighbor in the periodic table) in appearance, but is harder than iron and, unlike iron, is quite brittle. The ancient Romans confused pyrolusite with magnetite, the magnetic oxide of iron (see page 138), which is also black. So they called pyrolusite "magnes." In the Middle Ages, the alchemists somehow managed to misspell and mispronounce this name, and it ended up as "manganese." Manganese was first isolated as a metal by a chemist named J. G. Gahn in 1774.

Like chromium, manganese compounds are usually colored. There are naturally occurring manganese compounds in various colors (white, brown, green, violet) which artists have used as pigments for centuries. The most common is a chestnut-brown pigment made by grinding *manganese oxide* (its molecule contains two manganese atoms and three oxygen atoms) with iron and aluminum oxides. This is called *manganese brown*, or *umber*. *Manganese carbonate* (also called *manganese white*) is used as a white pigment.

The commonest ore of molybdenum is *molybdenite*, which is *molybdenum sulfide* (whose molecule contains one atom of molybdenum and two of sulfur). The ore has a leaden appearance and was therefore named with the Greek word for lead. The name, with the "um" ending, was transferred to the metal itself when that was discovered by P. J. Hjelm in 1782.

Wolfram was discovered twice. In 1781 Scheele discovered it in a mineral called *tung sten*, which is just Swedish for "heavy stone." This mineral, like barytes (see page 179), is twice as heavy as granite. It is now called scheelite in Scheele's honor. In 1783 the element was discovered independently by two brothers named Don Fausto and Don Juan José de Elhuyar in a mineral called *wolframite*. For this reason, the element has two names. "Wolfram" is its official name. In America and Great Britain, however, we are in the habit of calling it *tungsten* after the Swedish mineral. The man who first showed, in 1785, that the metals from scheelite and wolframite were the same was Rudolf Erich Raspe. He is far better known as the author of the Baron Munchausen stories.

All three of these metals can be added to steel. *Manganese steel*, containing 13 percent or less manganese, is very hard and tough and is used for the jaws of rock crushers, for instance. *Molybdenum steel*, containing 2 percent or more molybdenum, doesn't soften when hot and is used for high-speed cutting tools. This is also a use for *tungsten steel*, containing chromium and 7-20 percent wolfram, which stays hard even when red-hot. Tungsten steel is also used for armor plate and for special shells that will penetrate armor plate. Tungsten and chromium are also added to cobalt to form the very hard stellite alloys (see page 147). Molybdenum steel is extremely hard and is used in gun-barrels, armor-plate, bank vaults and so on.

Manganese can be added to copper to form *manganese bronze*. One such alloy, containing nickel also, is *manganin*, which is a poor conductor of electricity and is used in the same way as nichrome.

Manganese dioxide is black and is sometimes added to glass to neutralize the green color due to iron compounds. As the years pass, the manganese dioxide in such glass is converted to *sodium permanganate* (with a molecule containing one atom of sodium, one of manganese, and four of oxygen), the sodium atom and the extra oxygens coming from the sodium silicate in the glass. Sodium permanganate is a dark-purple compound, and so the glass takes on a delicate violet tinge. Certain houses in Boston have old, old windowpanes of this color, which are greatly valued by their owners as antiques.

Certain manganese alloys containing aluminum, tin, antimony and copper are strongly magnetic even though they contain no iron. In fact, an alloy of manganese and bismuth can form a magnet which is more difficult to demagnetize than any steel magnet. Some chromium alloys can also be used to make strong magnets. Such magnetic but iron-free alloys are called *Heusler's alloys* after the man who first discovered one, back in 1898.

Both manganese and molybdenum are essential trace

elements in living tissue. The need for tiny quantities of molybdenum in the human body was discovered only in the 1950s.

THE GLOWING FILAMENT

The wires, or filaments, in electric-light bulbs must possess two characteristics: they must conduct electricity poorly enough to heat up to a white glow when electricity passes through, and they must have such a high melting point that the heat doesn't melt them. (One needn't worry about their burning, since light bulbs are filled with argon.)

When Thomas A. Edison invented the electric light in 1879, he used carbon for the filament. It has the highest known melting point—about 3,500 degrees centigrade—of all substances, and it is a poor conductor. But, since it isn't a metal, it couldn't be drawn into a wire. It had to be deposited on cotton threads or bamboo fibers. Even though Edison kept the inside of the bulb a vacuum, the cotton or bamboo decomposed with the heat, and after a while the filament fell apart. The bulb had burnt out.

Osmium was tried after that, as I mentioned on page 202. Finally, wolfram was hit upon. Wolfram is nearly twice as good a conductor as the platinum metals, but it has a much higher melting point than osmium. Osmium melts at 2,700 degrees centigrade and wolfram at 3,370 degrees centigrade. Wolfram, in fact, is the highest-melting metal. Only carbon melts at a higher temperature.

The element just to the right of wolfram in the periodic table is *rhenium*, element No. 75. It is similar to wolfram in its properties but is very rare. There are some ores that are one-millionth rhenium and these are considered rich indeed, for most ores have far less. Rhenium wasn't discovered till 1925, and then it was discovered spectroscopically (like rubidium and cesium; see page 160) by a group of three German chemists, Walter Noddack, Ida Tacke, and Otto Berg. They knew exactly what they were looking for. By that time the periodic table was well established and chemists knew just where the holes for missing elements were located. Before rhenium was found, in fact, it was referred to as "dvi-manganese." "Dvi" is the Sanskrit word for "two" and the missing element was in "hole number two under manganese." There was also an "eka-manganese" in "hole number one," but I'll get to that later.

Noddack and the rest named the new element after the Rhine river (using its Latin name) in Germany.

Rhenium has a melting point of about 3,000 degrees centigrade, the second-highest melting point among metals. Since it conducts electricity only a fourth as well as wolfram, it would probably make very good electric-light filaments if only it weren't so rare. It is used in some fountain-pen points, however. Small quantities are all that are needed for that purpose.

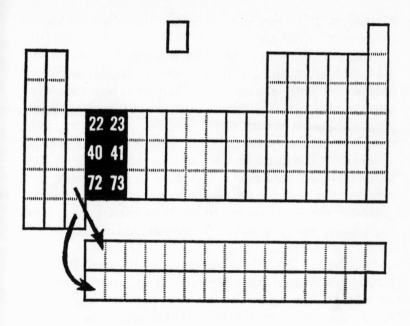

CHAPTER 20 **Titanium**

THE ELEMENT WITH A FUTURE

THE CINDERELLA METAL

In the entire periodic table there is probably no element that has been as unjustly neglected as *titanium,* element No. 22. Until quite recently, hardly anybody but professional chemists knew anything about it, and yet it is one of the commonest elements. One two-hundredth of the earth's crust is titanium. This may not seem like much, but it means ten pounds to the ton.

There is three times as much titanium as chlorine in the earth's crust, and six times as much titanium as phosphorus. Yet both chlorine and phosphorus are certainly common elements. Titanium is from sixty to three hundred times as common as such useful metals as copper, lead, and zinc. Yet, until very recently, titanium has been ignored.

There is one good reason for that. An element—lead, let us say—may be almost non-existent in most places yet pile up in a few places. In those few places it can be profitably mined. Titanium, on the other hand, is just scattered about pretty evenly. It's everywhere, but it's piled up hardly anywhere.

In 1791 an English clergyman and chemist, William Gregor, recognized the presence of a new metal in *ilmenite* (an ore containing both iron and titanium), and M. H. Klaproth named it in 1794. He called the element titanium after the mythical Titans, who were giants of enormous strength, but claimed in his writings to have no particular reason for doing so.

The most important titanium ore is *rutile*, which consists of *titanium dioxide* (its molecule contains one atom of titanium and two of oxygen). Titanium dioxide can occur as transparent gems, which, since 1949, can be prepared artificially. These rutiles bend light (see page 68) even more than diamonds do. If rutiles are properly cut, they sparkle and flash more brilliantly than diamonds. The trouble with rutiles is that they are not at all hard and so are fairly easily scratched.

Titanium dioxide powder, called *titanium white*, is the whitest substance known; that is, an ounce of it, mixed in the proper proportions with paint, will whiten a larger area than an ounce of any other white pigment. Furthermore, titanium dioxide is not poisonous and is not discolored by sulfur compounds. It is therefore replacing white lead.

Titanium tetrachloride (with a molecule containing one titanium atom and four chlorine atoms) is a liquid which, in contact with moist air, fumes strongly. It is, therefore, used in sky-writing and for setting up smoke-screens.

But it is titanium metal itself that is a kind of Cinderella. It was always looked upon as a brittle and useless metal, not good for anything much. The trouble was that nobody could get the metal really pure. Berzelius prepared it first as an impure black powder in 1825. Moissan (who first isolated fluorine) did better in 1895, but even his samples contained 2 percent carbon. Titanium, you see, will combine readily with oxygen, nitrogen, carbon, and silicon, the very elements it is most likely to come in contact with. Titanium will even burn in nitrogen and therefore has to be welded under helium.

It is usually prepared as an alloy with iron, *ferrotitanium*, and in that form its activity is made use of. It can be added in small quantities to molten steel to act as a "scavenger." The titanium combines with the tiny bits of oxygen and nitrogen trapped in the molten steel. Then, when the steel cools and solidifies, there are no tiny gas bubbles hidden within it to weaken it.

When titanium was finally prepared in pure form, it turned out to be a surprising metal. It isn't brittle at all, but malleable and tough. It resists corrosion, particularly if a very small quantity of palladium is added. Properly alloyed, it is the strongest metal of all for its weight. (That is, if a pound of titanium is drawn out into a bar a foot long, it will support more weight than a pound of steel drawn out into a bar a foot long. Since titanium is lighter than steel, a pound of titanium will make a thicker bar than a pound of steel will.)

Titanium is fairly light, too. It is only three-fifths as heavy as steel but twice as heavy as aluminum.

In short, titanium suddenly became glamorous. Industry is now working madly to find better ways of producing more and more pure titanium. There is every reason to expect that this neglected and "useless" metal will some day follow only iron and aluminum in importance. After all, it combines lightness and strength and one could hardly ask for more.

MORE HARD STEELS

The elements below titanium in the periodic table, and in the column to its right, resemble it in many ways, but none are nearly as common.

There is a mineral called *zircon*, which sometimes occurs in transparent form and can be used as a gem. Zircons can be bought quite cheaply and look very much like diamonds. The zircon gets its name from a French word that comes from a Portuguese word that comes from an Arabic word that comes from a Persian word meaning "gold-colored," for some zircons are yellowish.

In 1824 Berzelius isolated from the zircon a new metal, which he called *zirconium*, though as early as 1789 Klaproth had decided a new metal was present there. (The zircon is zirconium silicate.) Zirconium, element No. 40, is only a thirtieth as common as titanium, but it is still ten times as common as lead. Like titanium, it is hard and brittle when impure, malleable when pure. *Ferrozirconium*, an iron alloy containing 20 percent zirconium, is used as a scavenger.

Zirconium and titanium are both used in surgery in bone repair work. *Zirconium oxide* (its molecule contains one atom of zirconium and two of oxygen), sometimes called *zirconia,* is refractory and is used for furnace linings. It can also be used in place of the more expensive stannic oxide (see Chapter 17) as an opacifier in making enamels. Then, too, zirconium oxide absorbs x-rays strongly and is non-poisonous, so it can be used as barium sulfate is (see Chapter 14) in studying the digestive tract. Nor is this all. When heated, zirconium oxide emits an intense white light so it can be used as a kind of limelight (see Chapter 13) to project motion pictures, for instance. Also it is as resistant to temperature change as is quartz and can make good laboratory crucibles for that reason. Zirconium oxide is indeed an all-around substance.

Almost always, where you find zirconium, you also find about 1 percent or so of the element just below it in the periodic table. (In fact, it wasn't till just a few years ago that pure zirconium without this contaminating element had been obtained.) Chemists suspected the existence of this element, thanks to the periodic table. In 1911, a French chemist announced he had discovered the element that filled the hole beneath zirconium and named it *celtium* after the Celtic people (Gauls) who lived in France in Roman times. This turned out to be a false alarm.

In 1922, however, a Hungarian chemist, Georg von Hevesy, and a Danish physicist, Dirk Coster, who were investigating, in Copenhagen, a zircon that they had obtained from Norway, did finally discover this element. They named it *hafnium* from a Latinized form of the name of Copenhagen. Hafnium is always considered a very rare metal, but actually it is fifty percent commoner than lead. It is element No. 72.

The delay in finding it (a full century after zirconium)

is not really surprising. Scarcely any two elements in the entire list are as similar as zirconium and hafnium. To locate a little of one in a large quantity of the other was a difficult task. This also means that if zirconium or a zirconium compound is useful for some reason, hafnium or a similar hafnium compound can be used for the same purpose. However, hafnium, being rarer, is considerably more expensive than zirconium.

The element immediately to the right of titanium in the periodic table was discovered by a Swedish chemist, N. G. Sefström, in 1830, and he called it *vanadium* (element No. 23) after an old Scandinavian goddess called Vanadis. It is about as common as zirconium.

Titanium, zirconium, and vanadium are used in steel alloys. Zirconium steels are tough and bullet-proof. Vanadium steels (which also contain chromium) are very resilient. They can take shocks without distortion. Vanadium steel is therefore used in springs, axles, crankshafts, and driveshafts. Titanium, when added to steels, supplies toughness and resistance to wear; such alloys are used for rails.

The two metals beneath vanadium in the periodic table were discovered at about the same time. An English chemist, Charles Hatchett, studied a mineral that had been sent to England from Connecticut by Connecticut's first governor back in the seventeenth century. In 1801 he decided that it contained a new metal, which he called *columbium*, from Columbia, a poetic name for the United States derived from Christopher Columbus. Considering the origin of the mineral, it is an appropriate name, but it didn't stick.

A Swedish chemist, Anders G. Ekeberg, discovered element No. 73, which he called *tantalum* after a Greek mythological character named Tantalus, who was punished in Hades by being placed up to his chin in water, without being allowed to drink it (hence our word "tantalize"). The connection is that tantalum, even when placed in acid, didn't combine with it.

There was some question at first whether columbium is really a separate metal or just another form of tantalum. In 1844 a chemist named Heinrich Rose finally proved that columbium is a separate element, and he called it *niobium* after a Greek mythological character named Niobe, the daughter of Tantalus. Though "niobium" has been accepted as the official name of element No. 41, in the United States it is still usually called columbium.

The oxides of vanadium, niobium and tantalum are all high-melting and therefore can be considered "earths." In solution, these oxides form weak acids so they are called the *acid earths* and the metals themselves are the *acid earth metals*. (Remember that calcium and its relatives are the "alkaline earth metals.")

Niobium and tantalum are both inert metals and can be used to replace platinum in laboratory crucibles and such articles. Tantalum is better than platinum in some ways. It is more resistant to acid, and it melts at a higher temperature, 2,996 degrees centigrade. At one time it was used for electric-light filaments, but now it has been replaced by wolfram. Niobium, when added to stainless steel, improves its resistance to corrosion. Niobium carbide, zirconium carbide, tungsten carbide and tantalum carbide are all very hard substances that can be used as abrasives.

Tantalum is also used for repair work in the body, as in skull plates, because it, like zirconium, and titanium, is not affected by body fluids.

Tantalum and zirconium give off even more light when burning than does magnesium. They are therefore suitable for flash photography. Of course, they are more expensive than magnesium, which is a drawback.

Tantalum and niobium are the materials out of which

the tiny wires of the cryotron (which I mentioned in Chapter 4) are made. Certain alloys of niobium become superconductive at higher temperatures than any other known substances. They are superconductive (see Chapter 4) at temperatures as high as 18 degrees above absolute zero.

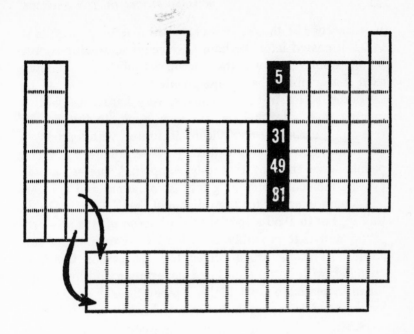

CHAPTER 21 **Boron**

THE DESERT ELEMENT

GLASS FOR COOKING

The other elements in the same column of the periodic table with aluminum are all quite rare. They certainly are unlike the very common aluminum in this respect. Some of them are unlike aluminum in other ways, too.

The element above aluminum in the periodic table, for instance, is *boron*, element No. 5, and it isn't even a metal.

It is one of the three non-metals that I left, on page 124, to be discussed later. Perhaps because of its small size, the boron atom resembles the carbon or silicon atom more than it resembles the aluminum atom.

Boron is, for instance, a black, very hard solid with a melting point of 2,300 degrees centigrade. In this way it resembles carbon. Like silicon, it forms, with carbon, a compound that resembles silicon carbide in hardness. Some people have thought that this compound, *boron carbide* (with a molecule containing four boron atoms and one carbon atom), was harder than diamond itself. That probably isn't so, but in 1956 a special kind of *boron nitride* was prepared, and that probably is as hard as diamond, perhaps harder. Its atoms are arranged like the carbon atoms in diamond, with boron atoms and nitrogen atoms alternating. It can be heated to much higher temperatures than diamond, for diamond burns while boron nitride does not.

Boron has a further connection with hardness. Small quantities of it added to steel, even as little as 1 part in 10,000, hardens steel considerably.

A compound of boron and phosphorus, with a molecule containing one atom of each is *boron phosphide*. It can be used as a transistor (see Chapter 17) at high temperatures which would break down ordinary transistors of silicon or germanium.

Boron resembles carbon also in forming a series of complex compounds with hydrogen. These *boron hydrides* are now being used to add more power to gasoline. They are also currently considered the best thing available for the powerful fuels needed for large rockets. In all, boron is another one of those first members of a group that resembles the adjacent group more than its own.

Boron oxide (with a molecule containing two atoms of

boron and three of oxygen) resembles silicon dioxide in some ways. It can be melted together with silicon dioxide to form *borosilicate glass.*

Borosilicate glass doesn't expand or contract as much as ordinary glass, and therefore doesn't crack, in going from a low to a high temperature or vice versa. It is not quite as good in this respect as quartz (see page 82), but glass-blowers find it easier to work with. For that reason, borosilicate products are much cheaper than quartz products.

A common trade name for this kind of glass is *Pyrex.* Most kitchens these days have Pyrex cooking vessels of various sorts. Such vessels can be heated directly over a gas flame or on an electric coil. Baby bottles made of borosilicate glass can be taken from a refrigerator and placed directly in a bottle warmer.

In chemical laboratories, also, borosilicate glass is very useful. Most laboratory beakers, flasks, and bottles are made out of Pyrex nowadays. The mirror of the 200-inch telescope at Mt. Palomar is made of a variety of Pyrex glass. Fine strands of Pyrex glass ("glass wool") can be handled as though they were cotton. As *Fibreglass,* they can even be woven into fire-proof fabric.

The best-known compound of boron is *borax.* Its chemical name is *sodium tetraborate,* and its molecule is made up of two sodium atoms, four boron atoms, and seven oxygen atoms. It has been known for a long time. The name "borax" came originally from the Persian language. When two French chemists, J. L. Gay-Lussac and L. F. Thenard, first isolated rather impure boron in 1808, they derived its name from the name of this familiar compound. So both boron and zirconium (see page 236) have names that we owe to the Persian language. Pure crystals of boron were not obtained till 1910.

Borax is useful as a water softener. Like sodium carbonate, it combines with compounds of calcium, magnesium, or iron that may be dissolved in the water, forming insoluble compounds that settle out of the water and become harmless. It is also used to prepare low-melting glazes for porcelain and enamel ware, and can be used as a flux (see Chapter 7) in soldering and welding.

The best sources of borax are the beds of certain dried-up lakes in the West. Some decades ago, Death Valley, in California, was the best source, and wagons hauled by the famous twenty-mule teams—ten pairs of mules yoked in a long line—went out to get it. Nowadays certain other dried-up lakes in California are better sources. It is for this reason, by the way, that I labeled boron a "desert element" in the chapter title.

Another familiar boron compound is *boric acid*. Its molecule contains three atoms of hydrogen, one of boron, and three of oxygen. It is such a weak acid that it might as well be considered no acid at all. It is a very mild antiseptic and is sometimes dissolved in water and used as an eye wash. If the delicate membranes of the eye can stand it, you can see how weak an acid it must be.

Boron is an essential trace element for plants, apparently. Animals, however, do not seem to need it.

PREDICTIONS AND PLATYPUSES

Just under aluminum in the periodic table is an element that serves as another example of the predicting power of the Russian chemist Mendeleev (see page 213). In 1871 he had pointed to the empty spot under aluminum and predicted the properties of the element (he called it *eka-aluminum*) that would fill the spot. When element No.

31 was discovered by a French chemist, P. E. Lecoq de
Boisbaudran, in 1875, Mendeleev turned out to be right.
The element was named *gallium,* from Gallia, the Roman
name for the country now called France. Of course, "Lecoq"
is French for rooster and "gallus" is Latin for the same
thing, and one wonders if de Boisbaudran might not have
named the element for himself.

Gallium has an unusually low melting point, 30 degrees
centigrade (86 degrees Fahrenheit). It is therefore a liquid
on a hot summer day, and a lump of it will melt in your
hand since body temperature is 37 degrees centigrade.
Gallium boils at 1,600 degrees centigrade. Some people
think it would make a good liquid for high-temperature
thermometers. Mercury, you see, isn't good for temperatures
over 350 degrees centigrade, for it boils at that point.

The two elements below gallium are *indium,* No. 49, and
thallium, No. 81. Both were discovered spectroscopically.
In 1863 two German chemists, Ferdinand Reich and Theo-
dor Richter, noted, in a flame spectrum, a new colored line
that belonged to no element then known. Because the
color of the line was indigo blue, they called the new
element indium. Indium is sometimes plated over silver to
prevent tarnish. It is one of the softest metals and can be
easily cut with a knife.

Previously, in 1861, a British chemist, Sir William
Crookes, had also noted a new line in a flame spectrum.
Since this one was green, he called the element thallium,
from the Greek word for "budding twig."

Thallium is an odd element. It resembles so many other
elements that chemists have called it the duckbilled platypus of the periodic table. (The duckbilled platypus is an
Australian animal that has fur like a mammal but lays eggs
like a bird or a reptile. It has a bill and webbed feet, like

a duck, but spurs on its hind legs, like a rooster. And the spurs are poisoned, like a snake's fangs.) Thallium isn't really as bad as all that, but it's bad enough to confuse chemists. Like lead, the metal is soft and heavy and melts at a low temperature. And its compounds are poisonous, as lead compounds are. (*Thallous sulfate*, which contains two atoms of thallium, one of sulfur, and four of oxygen in its molecule, is used as an ant poison. An early symptom of thallium poisoning is the falling out of the hair.) But thallium forms an oxide that resembles the oxides of manganese and aluminum rather than those of lead. And, to top it off, it forms other compounds that resemble those of sodium and potassium, elements that are nowhere near it in the periodic table.

If one part of thallium is mixed with eleven parts of mercury, the mixture doesn't freeze until a temperature of 60 degrees below zero centigrade is reached. I think this is the lowest freezing point on record for any metal or mixture of metals.

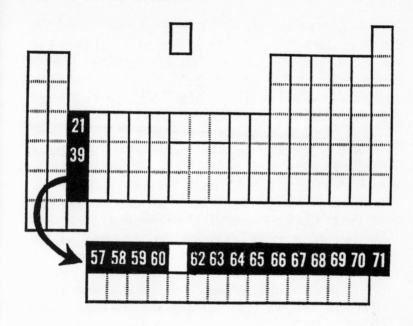

CHAPTER 22

Yttrium

THE SCANDINAVIAN ELEMENT

CROWDING THE PERIODIC TABLE

In 1794 a man named J. Gadolin, a native of Finland, found a new kind of mineral in Sweden, near the little town of Ytterby. He called it *yttria*. Eventually this mineral was found to contain a new element, which was, naturally enough, called *yttrium*. It is element No. 39.

The story doesn't end there, however. Later developments mystified chemists for a time. In 1843 a chemist named C. G. Mosander found that yttria could be separated into three parts with somewhat different chemical characteristics. One of the parts he still called yttria. The other two parts he called *terbia* and *erbia*, both names still coming from the little town of Ytterby.

Then, one by one, as the years passed, chemists began to find new elements in these minerals and in similar minerals. Finally a series of fifteen elements, with consecutive numbers from 57 to 71, had been discovered.

All these elements are similar to one another. They all have almost the same chemical characteristics. Worse than that, they all seem to belong in the same spot in the periodic table. Their behavior indicates that every one of them should be placed just under yttrium.

Naturally, this puzzled and bothered chemists. It upset the periodic table, which had been working nicely otherwise.

Fortunately, since 1900, chemists have learned a good deal about the inner structure of atoms. Now we know why these elements resemble one another, and we make a special place in the periodic table for them.

In a very general way, this is the explanation: The outer portions of an atom contain tiny particles (much tinier, even, than atoms themselves) called *electrons*. The number of electrons in the atoms of a particular element is equal to the number of that element. Yttrium, for instance, which is element No. 39, contains thirty-nine electrons in each atom. As we go through the periodic table from element No. 1 (hydrogen) on, new electrons are added to the outermost part of the atom. The chemical characteristics of an element depend upon the arrangement of these outermost electrons.

When element No. 57 is reached, for reasons that are a little too complicated to explain here, new electrons are added, not to the outermost part of the atom, but to the inner regions. The arrangement of the outer electrons remains the same for all the elements numbered from 57 to 71.

It is the arrangement of the outer electrons that decides where an element should be in the periodic table. The elements from 57 to 71 all seem to belong in the same place because their outer electron arrangements are the same. The inner electron arrangements are different, of course, but that doesn't matter very much as far as chemical characteristics are concerned.

It is as though you were seeing a group of fifteen families living in fifteen identical houses of a suburban development. All the houses would be the same, and the lots would be landscaped the same way. The families would all seem to be equally well-to-do. The way in which the houses were furnished would show differences among the families, but you wouldn't be able to tell that just by looking at the outside of the houses. The furnishings would be the "inner electrons." All that you would see would be the externals, the "outer electrons."

THE IDENTICALS

As I said earlier (page 166), the early chemists called the compounds of oxygen with certain metals "earths." Calcium oxide and magnesium oxide are "alkaline earths" while vanadium oxide and tantalum oxide are "acid earths." The oxides of the new elements in yttria were also called earths —*rare earths* because they are much less common than calcium oxide and magnesium oxide. The elements themselves are therefore called the *rare-earth elements*.

All the rare-earth elements put together are considerably more common than copper or lead. Some members of the series are commoner than tin, but others are rare indeed. Even the rare ones, however, are more common than gold or platinum.

Three of the rare-earth elements are named after Ytterby. These are *terbium*, No. 65; *erbium*, No. 68, and *ytterbium*, No. 70. Terbium and erbium were discovered by Mosander in 1843. He got them out of those parts of yttria that he had called terbia and erbia (see page 248). Ytterbium was discovered by J. C. G. de Marignac in 1878.

There is something rather dramatic about this. There is no element named after most of the great cities of the world. No element is named after London, New York, Moscow, Tokyo, Shanghia, Berlin, or Buenos Aires. There is one element named after Paris, to be sure, but only after an old version of its name. Yet here we have no less than four elements, yttrium, ytterbium, terbium, and erbium, all named after an obscure Swedish town that nobody outside its own vicinity had ever heard of before.

Two other elements of the rare-earth series have names derived from Scandinavian places. In 1879 a chemist named P. T. Cleve discovered the elements numbered 67 and 69. He called No. 67 *holmium* after Stockholm, the capital of Sweden. No. 69 he called *thulium* after Thule, an ancient name for a mysterious land of the far north, which he applied, poetically, to modern Scandinavia.

In 1880 Marignac discovered element No. 64, which he called *gadolinium* after Gadolin, the Finn who had first discovered yttria. So nearly half of the rare-earth elements have names with some Scandinavian connection, which is why I called yttrium the Scandinavian element in the chapter heading.

Gadolinium is unusual, by the way, in being weakly

magnetic. It is the only element with this property besides iron, nickel, and cobalt. None of the other rare-earth elements are magnetic.

Naturally, since the rare-earth elements are very much alike, chemists have always had a great deal of difficulty in separating one from another. (You know the difficulty there sometimes is in telling identical twins apart and the confusion that may arise. Well, imagine fifteen identical people.)

Chemists, being human, became exasperated. Element No. 57, discovered by Mosander in 1839, was named *lanthanum* from a Greek word meaning "to conceal." Lecoq de Boisbaudran was even more blunt; when he discovered element No. 66 in 1886, he called it *dysprosium* from a Greek word meaning "hard to get at."

Lanthanum is the first of the rare-earth elements, the one with the lowest element number. For this reason, the rare-earth elements are sometimes called the *lanthanides*. Lanthanum is one of the commoner rare earths. In appearance it rather resembles iron.

MORE IDENTICALS

Elements No. 59 and No. 60 were discovered by C. A. von Welsbach in 1885. He called No. 59 *praseodymium* from the Greek words for "green twin," because it forms green-colored compounds. He called No. 60 *neodymium* from the Greek words for "new twin." The "twin" in these names shows the similarity of the elements and how hard it is to separate them. Neodymium, like lanthanum, is one of the commoner rare earth elements.

In 1879 Lecoq de Boisbaudran discovered element No. 62 in a Russian mineral that had been named samarskite after a Russian mine official named Samarski. The discoverer called the new element *samarium,* thus immortalizing the Russian. Samarium is the hardest of the rare-earth elements, being as hard as some kinds of steel.

Some of the rare-earth elements weren't discovered till after 1900. In 1901 Eugène Demarçay discovered element No. 63, which he called *europium* after Europe. In 1907 G. Urbain discovered element No. 71, which he called *lutetium* from the old Roman name for Paris.

The commonest rare-earth element of all is No. 58. It was the first of the series to be discovered. Klaproth and Berzelius turned the trick in 1803 and named the element *cerium* after a small planetoid, Ceres, which had been discovered in the skies two years earlier. Cerium is the easiest of the rare-earth elements to separate from the rest, for it has a few chemical characteristics that the others don't have. By taking advantage of those, we can pull it right out of the mixture.

Cerium is common enough and easy enough to purify to have some practical uses. Before the days of the electric light, gas lights or kerosene lamps were used. These were dimmer than our modern bulbs, and yellower and flickering besides. In order to improve those lights, people put a perforated cylinder called a *gas mantle* round the flame. The mantle, in the heat of the flame, glowed with a light that was steadier, brighter, and whiter than the flame itself. One of the substances in this gas mantle was *cerium oxide,* the molecule of which contains two atoms of cerium and three of oxygen.

Cerium will burn with a bright white flame, much as magnesium will. This characteristic is also useful. Cerium and iron can be alloyed together (seven parts of cerium to three of iron) to form *ferrocerium* or *mischmetal.* Mischmetal is German for "mixed metal," because it does contain small quantities of the other rare-earth elements in addition to cerium. This is used in cigarette lighters. It gives off hotter sparks than iron or steel alone would give off and therefore sets fire more easily to the vapor of the lighter fluid. Rare earth metals, added to carbon, make for more brilliant arc lights.

During World War II it became necessary, in atomic bomb research, to figure out a way to separate the rare-earth elements quickly. To do this, chemists made use of ion-exchange resins (see page 172).

Solutions containing compounds of the different rare-earth elements were poured through a long column of particles of the resin. The different compounds stuck to the resin in different places and with different amounts of tightness. By proper treatment, they could be loosened one by one, and each could be separated from the rest. Now that this new method has solved the problem of teasing the rare-earth elements apart, new uses will probably be found for the commoner ones, cerium, lanthanum, and neodymium.

As it is, the rare-earth elements are being offered for sale in carload lots.

If you check through this chapter, you will see that I have not mentioned element No. 61. This is not an accident. I shall explain why in the next chapter.

One more element remains to be mentioned before I end the chapter. The rare earths are underneath yttrium in the periodic table. There is also an element just above yttrium. This is element No. 21 and it is the third element whose properties were correctly predicted by Mendeleev (see pages 214 and 245). It was discovered by L. F. Nilson in 1897 and named *scandium* after Scandinavia; and that is a good way to end a chapter devoted to "Scandinavian elements."

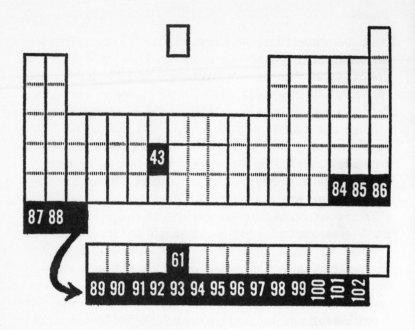

CHAPTER 23

Uranium

THE UNSTABLE ELEMENT

ATOMS THAT BREAK UP

So far in this book, I have discussed eighty-one different elements. These go from No. 1 (hydrogen) to No. 83 (bismuth). (That makes only eighty-one elements because No. 43 and No. 61 were left out.)

The eighty-one elements I've discussed have something in common. They are all *stable*; that is, if an atom of one of these elements is left to itself, it will remain an atom of the same element forever. These eighty-one elements, more-over, are all the stable elements we know, and it seems pretty certain that these eighty-one are the only stable elements that can possibly exist.

Yet these are not the only elements. At the very beginning of this book I said that there are 102 elements altogether. This leaves twenty-one elements to be accounted for. These twenty-one are all *unstable;* that is, an atom of any of these elements, if left to itself, will sooner or later change into some other kind of atom.

The commonest of these twenty-one unstable elements, the longest-known, and the most important is *uranium,* element No. 92. It was discovered by Klaproth in 1789 in a mineral called *pitchblende.* He named it after the newly discovered planet Uranus.

Pitchblende contains *uranium oxide,* the molecule of which consists of three atoms of uranium and eight of oxygen. Uranium is very difficult to purify. Like titanium and similar metals (see page 235), it is so active that it holds on to impurities tightly. Uranium was not prepared as the pure metal until 1942, when it was desperately needed for atomic bomb research. The metal is silvery in color and is almost as heavy as gold.

There wasn't much use for uranium for a hundred years after it was discovered. For instance, the pitchblende deposit in Czechoslovakia was mined from the 16th century on for the silver it contained. In the 19th century, just about all the silver was gone, but for a while it was still mined for its lead content. Then that, too, was abandoned. No one cared about the fact it contained uranium; at least not until the 1940's.

Some uranium compounds, if added to glass, give the glass a canary-yellow color. Some uranium compounds can also be used as a porcelain paint. That is about all the uranium uses and it isn't much, is it? Even chemists were interested in the element only because some of its compounds fluoresced; that is, under ultraviolet rays they glowed a luminous yellow.

Then, in 1896, quite by accident, a French physicist named A. H. Becquerel discovered that uranium atoms give off strange radiations of a kind never observed before. (This kind of behavior was later called *radioactivity*.) Almost at once, uranium became interesting. Many chemists and physicists started studying it.

It was found that some of the uranium radiations consist of particles much smaller even than atoms. These are called *sub-atomic particles*. Other radiations are like X-rays, only stronger. Some scientists died from the effect of the radiations of uranium and similar elements before people realized how dangerous radioactivity can be.

As a result of studying these radiations, scientists learned a good deal about the insides of atoms. They found out that atoms are made up of sub-atomic particles of various kinds. They found out how to use these sub-atomic particles to change one kind of atom into another. (Such changes are called *nuclear reactions*.) They found out how to build *atomic piles* to produce usable energy out of nuclear reactions. They even found out how to build *atomic bombs*. Now the ignored and seemingly useless uranium is one of the most valuable of the elements—and certainly the most frightening.

One of the first things they found out was that uranium atoms are breaking up all the time. Each uranium atom, sooner or later, throws off, with great force, some of the sub-atomic particles that make it up. These flying particles are the radiations that Becquerel detected. When a uranium atom does this, it stops being uranium and becomes another kind of atom.

You may wonder why there is still uranium in existence if uranium atoms are always breaking up. The answer to that is that the break-up is happening very slowly. Each uranium atom breaks up sooner or later, but usually later, much later. In every ounce of uranium more than a million atoms are breaking up every second. But atoms are so small, and there are so many of them in an ounce of uranium, that it will take nearly five billion years before that ounce of uranium is even half gone. Since the earth is less than four billion years old, most of the original uranium is still with us. What's more, it will stay with us for many, many more years unless we ourselves use it up for atomic energy.

An element similar to uranium in its characteristics is *thorium,* element No. 90. It was discovered by Berzelius in 1828 in a Norwegian mineral called *thorite,* which had been named after an old Norse god, Thor. Thorite contains *thorium silicate,* the molecule of which contains one atom of thorium, one of silicon, and four of oxygen. In the United States there is a thorium-containing mineral called *monazite,* which contains *thorium dioxide* (more commonly called *thoria*), whose molecule contains one atom of thorium and two of oxygen.

Thorium dioxide was used in gas mantles, which I mentioned on page 252 . A gas mantle, in fact, was 99 percent thorium dioxide; but, since pure thorium dioxide gave only a feeble light when heated, cerium oxide (1 percent) was added to increase the brilliance of the light. Although gas mantles have been largely replaced by incandescent electric lights, they are still used in places. The street next to the one on which I live is lighted by gas mantles and the people living there won't allow them to be replaced, either. They are quaint, and New Englanders are fond of quaintness.

Thorium oxide is a refractory substance and a bit of it added to tungsten will lengthen the life of electric light filaments.

Thorium is radioactive, as uranium is, and gives off the same kind of radiations. Thorium breaks up even more slowly than uranium does, however. Since the earth was formed, only about one-fifth of its thorium has had a chance to break up.

RADIOACTIVE DESCENDANTS

When uranium or thorium atoms break up, they change into other types of atoms. These, being also radioactive, break up into still other atoms, which also are radioactive. Finally, after more than a dozen steps, a stable atom is formed. This stable atom is, of all things, a lead atom!

Among the atoms that are formed on the way from uranium or thorium (elements 92 and 90) to lead (element number 82) are all the elements with numbers from 84 to 91. These are all radioactive elements and are not stable. Furthermore, they all break up much more rapidly than uranium or thorium. If these elements from 84 to 91 existed by themselves, even in large quantities, they would be all gone in a few million years at most. Some would be gone in a few days. None of them, certainly would exist now, with the earth nearly four billion years old, if fresh supplies of them were not continually being formed from uranium and thorium.

Naturally, then, all the minerals that contain uranium or thorium also contain a little of each of these *daughter elements*. For this reason, pitchblende is still radioactive after all the uranium is removed from it. The daughter elements are still there.

Pierre and Marie Curie, a husband-and-wife team, worked with pitchblende from which the uranium had been removed. They tried to separate the elements that gave rise to the radiations that were still left. You can imagine how difficult this was when I tell you that the radioactive daughter elements in pitchblende amount to less than one part in three million. A ton of pitchblende contained only about 1/1,000 ounce of what they were looking for. Fortunately, they had two truckloads of ore to work with. The Austrian government (which then ruled in Czechoslovakia) gave them the "useless" stuff for practically nothing. The Curies had to pay transportation, though, and that took almost all the money they had.

And they found what they were looking for. In 1898 they discovered *polonium*, element No. 84, which they named after Madame Curie's native country, Poland. Later that year they discovered *radium*, element No. 88 in compound form. They prepared radium metal in 1910. Its name is derived from the Latin word for "ray." Both elements are much more strongly radioactive than uranium or thorium. The strong radiations from radium have been used to kill cancer cells in the human body, but this must be done very carefully because the radiations can also cause cancer. (Nowadays we have better and safer ways of using radioactivity for such purposes.)

Although these elements are unstable, they take their place in the periodic table along with the stable elements. Radium is an alkaline-earth element. It fits just under barium and is very similar to barium in its chemical characteristics. Polonium fits under tellurium and is similar to it in its chemical characteristics.

When the radium atom breaks up, it forms an atom of *radon*, element No. 86. Radon is a gas, a radioactive gas! It fits into the inert gas column of the periodic table, right under xenon, and has all the chemical characteristics of the other inert gases.

Radon was first discovered in 1900 by a chemist named F. E. Dorn, and he called it *radium emanation* because it emanated from (that is, was given off by) radium. Ramsay and R. Whytlaw-Gray collected the gas in 1908, and they called it *niton* from a Greek word meaning "shining." In 1923, though, the official name became "radon" to show that the gas arose from radium.

In 1899 a chemist named A. L. Debierne discovered element No. 89, which he called *actinium* from the Greek word for "ray." Then, in 1917, two different pairs of chemists (Frederick Soddy and J. A. Cranston in England and Otto Hahn and Lise Meitner in Germany) announced the discovery of element No. 91. Since element No. 91, when it breaks up, gives rise to actinium, it was called *protactinium*. The "prot" part of the name comes from a Greek word meaning "first"; in other words, actinium was protactinium first.

Other gases arise from the breakdown of thorium and actinium (I will mention the latter in a moment) and have been called *thoron* and *actinon*, respectively. These are, as it turns out, varieties of radon. However, there have been suggestions that the element be named *emanon* (from "emanation") since it does not arise from the breakdown of radium only, as "radon" implies.

This still left elements 85 and 87 to be accounted for. These two, however, are so unstable and break up so quickly that very little of them is left behind. For many years, therefore, no trace of them was found.

THE LAST HOLES

After 1925, when rhenium was discovered, there were only four holes left in the periodic table. These belonged to elements numbered 43, 61, 85, and 87. Elements 85 and 87 were obviously radioactive elements, and people thought they might be very unstable and therefore hard to find.

The case was different for elements 43 and 61. They were surrounded by stable elements, and everyone thought they should be stable, too. There was quite a search for them for that reason.

Element No. 43 is just above rhenium in the periodic table. In 1925 the same German chemists who discovered rhenium (see page 232) announced the discovery of element No. 43. This was the "eka-manganese" I mentioned in connection with rhenium at the end of Chapter 19. They called it *masurium* after a district in eastern Germany called Masuria. We know now that element 43 is unstable. Furthermore, since it isn't formed from any other element, none of it is found in the soil. The chemists who announced masurium must therefore have been mistaken.

The same thing happened with element No. 61 in a kind of double fashion. Certain American chemists announced its discovery in 1926 and called it *illinium* after the state of Illinois. Certain Italian chemists claimed they had discovered it first and called it *florentium* after the Italian city of Florence. There was quite an argument about it, but both groups of chemists must have been mistaken. Element No. 61 is even more unstable than element No. 43, and none of it exists in the soil.

But how do we know about elements 43 and 61 if they don't exist in the soil? In 1919 a British scientist named Ernest Rutherford first learned how to change one kind of atom (even a stable one!) into another kind by bombarding it with sub-atomic particles. With the years, improvements were made in the process, and scientists grew quite skilled at manufacturing new kinds of atoms.

Eventually, in 1937, two young chemists, C. Perrier

and E. Segré, studied a sample of element 42 (molyb-denum) that had been bombarded with subatomic particles and had found in them newly-created atoms of a brand-new element, one that did not exist on the earth. This was molyb-denum's neighbor in the periodic table, element No. 43, and they called it *technetium* from a Greek word meaning "artificial." Enough of the element was made so that its characteristics could be studied. Technetium is now the official name for element No. 43, and "masurium" is dead and gone. Technetium was the first *artificial element* to be made.

In 1948 three chemists, J. A. Marinsky, L. E. Glendenin, and C. D. Coryell, produced atoms of element No. 61 and called it *promethium* after Prometheus, the Greek Titan who had brought fire down from the sun for the use of mankind. (They were probably thinking of the atomic fire of the A-bomb, which, after all, is really the kind of fire that does light the sun.) Promethium is now the official name of the element.

As for elements 85 and 87, an American chemist an-nounced in 1931 that he had detected them. He called element 85 *alabamine* and element 87 *virginium* after the states of Alabama and Virginia. Most other chemists re-mained doubtful.

Of all the elements, technetium becomes superconduc-tive at the highest temperature (11 degrees above absolute zero) though some alloys (but not pure elements) can do a bit better. Certain technetium compounds, called *pertechne-tates* are very efficient in preventing iron and steel from corroding. For the purpose, the metal need only be dipped into pertechnetate solution. Technetium is too rare and expensive for this ever to be a commercial process. However, chemists are studying this intensively in order to learn more about corrosion.

In 1939 a French chemist named Marguerite Perey definitely detected element No. 87 among uranium breakdown products. She called it *actinium K* at first, but eventually named it *francium* after France. Her evidence was accepted and "francium" was adopted as the official name. The next year, 1940, D. P. Corson, K. R. Mackenzie, and E. Segré produced element No. 85, which they called *astatine* from a Greek word meaning "unstable." That is the official name for the element now.

Astatine and francium are both members of well-known families of elements. Francium is an alkali metal that fits into the periodic table just below cesium. Astatine is a halogen that fits into the periodic table just below iodine.

Astatine and radon are the only unstable elements that are non-metals. You see that both have been given names that end in "ne" or "n." With these we end the list of non-metals at a total of twenty-two. Astatine was detected among uranium breakdown products in 1943.

HIGHER THAN THE HIGHEST

By 1948 the last hole in the periodic table had been filled, and yet the discovery of new elements didn't stop. For 150 years uranium (element No. 92) had been considered the last element, but, after all, why shouldn't there be elements with numbers higher than 92?

It turns out there is no reason why there shouldn't be. A group of American scientists, of whom G. T. Seaborg is the best-known, have been producing element after element with atomic numbers higher than 92. They work at the University of California in Berkeley, where technetium and astatine, among the elements lower than 92, had been produced. Promethium had been produced in Oak Ridge, Tennessee.

As a group, these elements beyond uranium in the periodic table are known as the *transuranium elements*. All the transuranium elements are quite unstable and (with one exception) do not exist naturally in the soil.

In 1940 elements 93 and 94 were produced. Since element 92, uranium, had been named after the planet Uranus, elements 93 and 94 were named after the planets beyond Uranus. These are Neptune and Pluto. Element 93 was therefore called *neptunium,* and element 94 was called *plutonium.* E. M. McMillan and P. Abelson were the first to detect a transuranium element. In 1951, McMillan and Seaborg were awarded the Nobel Prize for Chemistry, for their work on the transuranium elements.

Uranium atoms occasionally break up in such a way that plutonium atoms are formed. Very small quantities of plutonium have actually been detected in uranium ores. So plutonium is the one transuranium element that exists naturally, and it is also the naturally occurring element with the highest atomic number. Artificial plutonium, however, has been created in such quantities that pounds and pounds of it can be used in atomic power plants and in atomic bombs.

It has been found that plutonium actually occurs in nature. Uranium ores always contain plutonium but not much. There is only one hundred-trillionth as much plutonium in the ores as uranium. It arises from certain radioactive transformations that uranium undergoes. Neptunium should also occur, but it would be present in even smaller quantities than plutonium.

It was noticed almost at once that neptunium and plutonium have chemical characteristics very like those of uranium and thorium. Chemists decided they were faced with a "rare-earth" situation again—that is, with a series of very similar elements.

Since this new series begins with actinium, the elements are called the *actinides*, just as those of the first series are called the lanthanides (see page 251). The actinides are placed immediately under the lanthanides in the periodic table: actinium under lanthanum, thorium under cerium, protactinium under praseodymium, uranium under neodymium, neptunium under promethium, and plutonium under samarium.

The men at the University of California continued to produce new elements. In 1944 element No. 95 was discovered. Since it fits under europium, it was named *americium* after America as a kind of balance. In 1946 element No. 96 was discovered. This fits under gadolinium, which had been named after a chemist who was important in the early history of the rare-earth elements (see page 250). So element No. 96 was named *curium* after the Curies, who were important in the early history of radioactivity (see page 259).

Actinides are similar to lanthanides in some chemical properties. Thorium, for instance, is usually found in ores containing lanthanides. *Monazite,* which is the chief thorium ore, contains the lanthanides as well. Chemical processes that concentrate a particular element in a particular place in the earth will also work to concentrate any elements with similar properties in the same place. That's why all the lanthanides are found together, why hafnium occurs in zirconium ores, why cadmium occurs in zinc ores, why the platinum metals occur in nickel mines and so on.

Element No. 97 was discovered in 1949 and element No. 98 in 1950. These were called *berkelium* and *californium* after the city and state where all this was happening.

In 1954 elements 99 and 100 were discovered. They were officially named late in 1955. Element 99 is called *einsteinium* after the German scientist Albert Einstein, and element 100 is called *fermium* after the Italian scientist Enrico Fermi. (Both became naturalized American citizens in later life.) Both Einstein and Fermi made important discoveries that led to a better understanding of the atom.

In 1955, element 101 was discovered, and it was named *mendelevium* after the Russian chemist, Mendeleev, who had first worked out the periodic table. Finally, in 1957, a team of American, British and Swedish scientists, working at the Nobel Institute for Physics at Stockholm, formed element 102. They named it *nobelium*, after the Institute, which was itself named after Alfred Nobel, the great Swedish explosives expert who invented dynamite and who, at his death, put aside a trust fund to establish the famous Nobel Prizes.

Will any more elements be discovered? Perhaps! Discovery is getting harder and harder all the time because each new transuranium element is more unstable than the one before and harder to work with. Chemists have some interest, though, in trying to reach as high as element No. 104. The reason for this is that the element numbered 103 should end the actinide series. Then element No. 104 should have new and different characteristics and be located under hafnium in the periodic table. This would be one last proof of the usefulness of the table. Still, even if element 104 isn't reached, chemists scarcely need further proof.

So there you have it. The rollcall is complete. One hundred and two different elements (eighty-one of them stable), out of which everything in the universe is composed, including you and me and the farthest star.

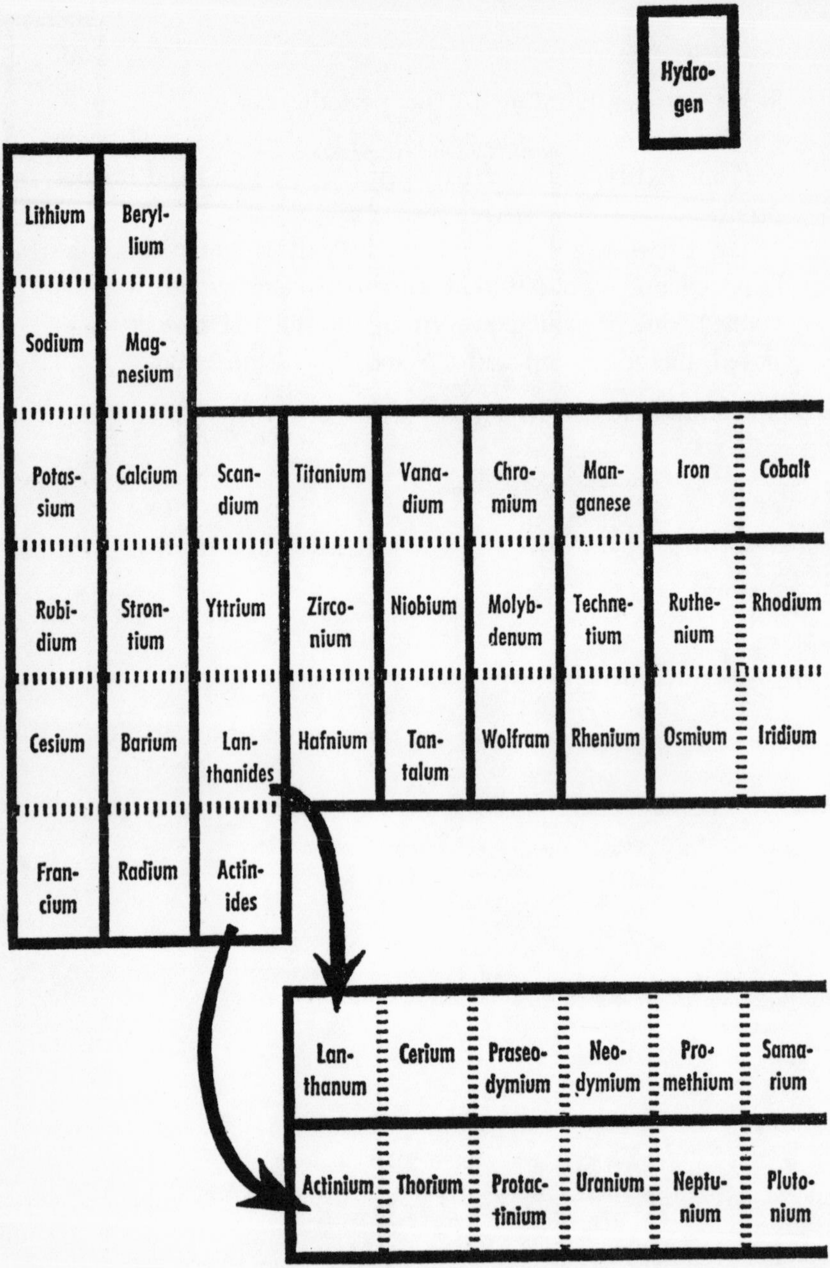

Hydrogen
Lithium
Beryllium
Sodium
Magnesium
Potassium
Calcium
Scandium
Titanium
Vanadium
Chromium
Manganese
Iron
Cobalt
Rubidium
Strontium
Yttrium
Zirconium
Niobium
Molybdenum
Technetium
Ruthenium
Rhodium
Cesium
Barium
Lanthanides
Hafnium
Tantalum
Wolfram
Rhenium
Osmium
Iridium
Francium
Radium
Actinides
Lanthanum
Cerium
Praseodymium
Neodymium
Promethium
Samarium
Actinium
Thorium
Protactinium
Uranium
Neptunium
Plutonium

								Helium
			Boron	Carbon	Nitrogen	Oxygen	Fluorine	Neon
			Aluminum	Silicon	Phosphorus	Sulfur	Chlorine	Argon
Nickel	Copper	Zinc	Gallium	Germanium	Arsenic	Selenium	Bromine	Krypton
Palladium	Silver	Cadmium	Indium	Tin	Antimony	Tellurium	Iodine	Xenon
Platinum	Gold	Mercury	Thallium	Lead	Bismuth	Polonium	Astatine	Radon

Europium	Gadolinium	Terbium	Dysprosium	Holmium	Erbium	Thulium	Ytterbium	Lutetium
Americium	Curium	Berkelium	Californium	Einsteinium	Fermium	Mendelevium	Nobelium	

INDEX